M000118972

URBAN DOG

URBAN DOG

THE ADVENTURES OF PARKER

WILL COHU

SIMON & SCHUSTER
A VIACOM COMPANY

The Daily Telegraph

First published in Great Britain by
Simon & Schuster UK Ltd, 2000
A Viacom Company

1 3 5 7 9 10 8 6 4 2

Simon & Schuster UK Ltd
Africa House
64–78 Kingsway
London WC2B 6AH

Simon & Schuster Australia
Sydney

A CIP catalogue record for this book is available
from the British Library

ISBN 0-684-86674-9

Typeset by Palimpsest Book Production Limited,
Polmont, Stirlingshire
Printed and bound in Great Britain by
The Bath Press, Bath

For Georgie

INTRODUCTION

Urban Dog began running in the *Weekend Section* of the *Daily Telegraph* in April 1998. I thought then that it would probably last for six months at the most and would be quickly forgotten – but more than a year on, I was sitting down to write a book based on it.

When I did the first columns, it seemed to me that I would soon exhaust the gamut of canine behaviour. After all, what does a dog do – my dog, at any rate – other than sniff, pee and wag his tail? As it happened, no one seemed to mind that I banged on about the same things from time to time. Doggy people wrote to me and shared their obsessions with these aspects of canine behaviour, and even some who *didn't* have dogs wrote to say that they found the sheer irrelevance of the column a reassuring fixture of their week's reading. Parker received more mail than me. The divergence and geographical extent of his post-bag never ceased to surprise me. Other dogs wrote offering love, weekends away or trial packages of new biscuits, and his correspondents included Scotties in Spain, Central Africa and the Far East.

I wasn't a great reader of other diary columns. When I did read them, I soon realised that most of them were repetitious, too, and that humans do pretty much the same things as dogs, with the addition of arguments in restaurants. All the same, I was afraid of being boring, and so went to strenuous efforts to make the thing as weird as I could. I found that I could encompass reflections on animal consciousness, sentimental descriptions of pets' behaviour and inconsequential anecdotes about humans without the readers raising an eyebrow. My editors at the *Daily Telegraph* only hooted their appreciation and encouraged me to further excesses of doggy madness. (I have to say that only the *Daily Telegraph* would have been radical enough to countenance a column about a Scottie dog in the first place.)

The original joke of the column was 'sad man living alone with dog' and I set out to write it – I hoped – with childish simplicity and tenderness about Dog-world and its inhabitants. At first I didn't have to try too hard to sound sad, but things changed and in time, I realised that I couldn't keep up the pretence of me and my dog against the world, so I began to write about other things and even about my life outside the dog. I often felt a strain in being dependent on him to provide me with material, and longed for a normal relationship with him: just having a dog, for dog's sake, not as a source of income. I also wondered if he was ever tired of being misrepresented, the way I suppose that the human families of other diarists become sick of being caricatured. At the same time I know that some diary columnists are able on occasion to subcontract their pieces to their loved ones, and I wished that Parker could contribute the occasional thought. It was a long time, though, before he found a voice and even then it was rather huffy.

Since I became a diary columnist, I've been haunted by the idea for a story in which a diarist who writes about his family finds that the two worlds – the one that appears in the newspaper and the one that they live –

begin far apart but gradually merge until everything he makes up in the column really begins to happen. The column, the life lived on the page, eventually takes over completely and real people exist only to provide the column with jokes. So I wrote little about myself. In this book, I wanted to fill in the gaps, and make it as whole as possible. My first efforts at a more autobiographical approach turned out to be both venomous and immensely self-castigating. I had to learn to adopt a less punishing tone. A book about a pet terrier is hardly the vehicle for splenetic confessional. So here it is at last, the book of the column, treading a line between biography and fiction, keeping the mundane bubbling at the point of whole-hearted fantasy, without ever permitting it to boil over.

It is, however, true in spirit. Though Parker is the main character – a prince among dogs, a special dog, as every doggy person thinks of their particular pet – in writing about him, I am still revealing more than I care to about myself.

Dog-owners often make remarkable claims for their pets: that they can predict earthquakes and fires, tell good people from bad at a look, sense danger and always know when their owner turns into the driveway. This seems like a fantasy to me. Personally I *don't* think that dogs have supernatural powers of perception, nor that they are intelligent in the sense that they are self-aware and able to reflect on their experiences. They do have feelings, though, and their senses are infinitely more acute than ours. Perhaps it's this preoccupied sensitivity that gives the appearance of thought.

For me, one of the most remarkable things about my Scottie is that he's a descendant of the grey wolf. Thousands of years of evolution and selective breeding have refined him into a creature two and a half feet long and a foot high, with thick black hair that curls when it's uncut. He has a long, square-ended nose, the shape and colour of a shoe-brush, and big, shiny-brown, expressive eyes – 'gorilla eyes' as my sister Lucy calls them. His whiskers are long, and as I've often said, frequently stiff and smelly, and he has an articulate tail that registers each degree of threat or excitement. When he stands at ease, his paws stick out nonchalantly to either side. He's got a sweet nature, except where matters of territorial dispute are concerned – disagreements over who owns the lamp-post across the road, for instance. Some of his poses suggest knowing arrogance. Just now, he's lying feet-up on the sofa. He didn't move when I offered him a dog-chew, but let it hang out of the corner of his mouth as if he was chomping on a cigar. It's at moments like this that I find him at his most human. I half-expect him to sit up and dictate terms for his continued co-operation.

I realise that I've imbued him with a character that is moody and slightly obsessive but determined, playful and in his heart of hearts, thoroughly optimistic – the better bits of myself, in fact. His true character is in his breeding. He's a terrier. He likes to shake socks to death, has a stubborn nature and can't easily be taught. He has a short concentration span for things that don't interest him but he never gives up on a good sniff.

Perhaps some of these apply to me, though whether I was always that way, I can't say. I simply know that I'm not the man I was before I got the dog. Thank you, Mr P.

I owe many people thanks for making the column and this book possible: my colleagues, past and present at the *Daily Telegraph,* in particular Kate Summerscale for her open mind and sympathetic editing of my early efforts; my agent, Mary Pachnos and all at Simon & Schuster. A special debt is owed to all those dogs, and their owners, who have filled the column, week after week. A big woof to you all.

Will Cohu

1

Parker came from Wales. He was born on a farm west of Carmarthen and I took him away at three months old, a tubby little black puppy, to be a friend for another Scottie called Pip who belonged to my girlfriend Catherine. I fancy that most dog-owners who have their pets as puppies say that the dogs chose them, and I was sure that Parker had run to me across the kitchen floor of the farm. He slept on my shoulder all the way home and afterwards he used to sleep on my feet as I worked.

He was quite defiant and independent at times, very affectionate, and he loved his food, eating slowly and studiously. We once fed him some chicken nuggets left over from a car journey and he sat back on his haunches in between bites and howled with pleasure. He never seemed to be troubled by new circumstances, and had a nose for a comfortable spot: he's always preferred the trailing sleeve of a cashmere sweater to a well-padded dog basket.

His proper name was Tweedie of Harrismoor, but I called him Parker after Lady Penelope's chauffeur in *Thunderbirds*.

Pip was bossy towards the puppy but there was never any trouble between the two dogs. It was always understood that Pip was leader of the pack. They were very different characters. Parker liked to curl up in dark corners and his big eyes could be seen glowing under the kitchen table or round the back of the sofa. Pip liked to settle himself on his back on chairs. Pip yipped and Parker barked. Pip was irrepressibly cheerful but Parker could be sensitive. If he was spoken to harshly, he would hang his head, look doubtful, and hide. He once nipped me when the bin had been emptied and I tried to extricate him from under the kitchen table for interrogation.

Pip liked to run away to the wild woods, vanishing for hours. Parker could generally be found hanging around the back gate, sniffing.

Rather to my surprise, I found I adored the dog, and even wrote a poem about him.

> *This dog is like me as a child –*
> *Shy, resentful, lazy, sly.*
> *First to the bowl, last to the gate,*
> *Short in the legs and overweight.*

At the time I was living in the Welsh Borders. I had originally gone to Wales for a holiday and ended up staying for a year, moving in with Catherine whom I'd met there. From the first, dogs had been part of our relationship. We'd been introduced to each other on a farm estate owned by mutual friends, whose old brown spaniel Brandy had attached himself to us when we went walking.

Brandy had been dumped by an uncle years before, and he largely fended for himself. He slept under the barn and his job was to retrieve the tennis balls knocked off court on Sunday mornings. The housekeeper fed him, but he was also adept at ingratiating himself with guests who would take him up for a while.

Brandy was brown and white and black all over. Stiff in the hind legs he stumbled over the surrounding hills, clouds of red mud billowing off him. He tagged along with anyone going walking. Often he carried a tennis ball with him, and the woods were littered with decayed Slazengers and Dunlops.

Brandy moved himself in with us, into a flat down in one corner of the farmyard. It was a smelly place, as the yard drains were either side of the front door. When it rained, tributaries of red mud flowed down the hill, uniting in a wide river. If the drains were blocked, the water came straight under the front door and swamped the flat in minutes. The walls had tidemarks and the carpet a warm earthy stink.

After our second flood, the drains were found to be blocked by one of Brandy's tennis balls. Perhaps it wasn't deliberate, but he did become jealous after Pip arrived.

Pip, the first Scottie, came from a Welsh farming family out west. The father was a man-mountain in a cloth cap, with a Rothmans wedged in his mouth. He sat by the fire, his lap filled with Scotties, asking them to 'give your dad a kiss'. I didn't realise until much later how peculiarly doggy-mad Scottie-owners are. The first thing I noticed about Pip was that he had a very long pink tongue. Despite the fierce reputation of his breed, the little Scot was more Robert the Bruce than William Wallace. The moment he arrived, he vanished – to be found, hours later, with the spiders under the cooker. He soon lost his fear, however, and began to roam, growing into a sinewy little dog, his short thick coat combed backwards from brambles, an exuberant, almost crazed look in his eyes. He showed a taste for corrupt company, scrounging for eggs in the barns in the company of Brandy and a slinky black Labrador called Bubbles.

Sometimes a chicken would go missing. An inquisition would follow, and blame would be assigned according to which dog-owner was not in favour. Everybody knew it was Bubbles who had a taste for poultry, but Bubbles belonged to the daughter of the house.

The estate was a beautiful place, and very wild. The chickens ran wild, the dogs ran wild and the children ran wild. Pip dashed here and there, stopping only to go belly-up asleep, paws in the air. On sunny days he hung around the farmyard. He was fascinated by the horses and would eat the hoof-clippings after the blacksmith had been.

Within a few months, Catherine, Pip and I had moved a mile or so away to a house on an adjacent hilltop. It had an orchard and a small pond with some goldfish. Despite these attractions, Pip was lonely and persisted in running back to see his old dog-friends on the farm. Word came that he was liable to be shot for chicken chasing and so Parker arrived to keep him company. Shortly afterwards, Catherine went off to a garden centre to buy plants and came back with a small, witchy black cat who we called Polly.

Parker liked Polly. He would snuggle up next to her when possible and practised being a cat, going in and out of the cat-flap. His fat bottom would sometimes get stuck halfway. Polly used to tease the dogs, letting her tail hang off the edge of chairs then whisking it out of reach, and in the evenings they played chase, sliding across the waxed wooden floor or zipping up- and downstairs, their tails standing up like the aerials on a pair of police motor-cycles. Polly even went for walks with them.

The dogs spent their days running from one gate to the other, barking at passing dogs and horses, or rootling in the orchard. Pip sat by the pond, staring at the goldfish; Parker chewed things – cardboard boxes and the bottom of my study door. He chewed a hole in my Wellingtons. Nearby was a small post-office, and a clutch of Jack Russell terriers lay outside in the dust. Pip fought them; Parker howled then ran away. They hunted rabbits together. Pip would go into the hedgerow while Parker sat outside waiting to pounce and showed a surprising turn of speed in pursuit. He did once catch a rabbit, though it had a broken leg.

When we went walking, Pip dashed ahead, then dashed back, urging me to keep up. Parker galloped behind, unco-ordinated, his back legs going one way, his front another. His bum wobbled. At some point in the course of a walk, Pip would take off rabbiting, his yips of excitement becoming fainter and fainter, until he vanished altogether among the dense stands of conifers that clothed the hillsides. On the odd occasion that Parker tried to keep up with him, he became lost and several times I traced his plaintive squeaks to a thicket of brambles. In those moments standing in the wood, waiting for Parker, I began to feel dreadfully upset at the thought of losing him and realised I had fallen for the odd little dog.

Sometimes we went to London. Pip didn't much care for Town. London was good for sniffs, but Pip was never a great sniffer. If the dogs were left alone in London, Pip was liable to protest, emptying the vegetable rack and putting potatoes in any shoes that were around. I hated leaving them alone and made a terrible scene when we went away to Ireland on holiday and learned that the dog-sitter had neglected them.

*   *   *

The house Catherine and I shared was in a little hamlet scattered over a small area of common woodland and meadow; it was both secluded and curiously suburban – a mixture of old cottages and new brick bungalows set up among the woods and meadows, as if an encampment of tents had over the course of centuries turned to brick and mortar. People kept an eye out for each other, and an eye *on* each other – and I soon gathered from gossip that many couples had come up there to escape the rat race, but few had survived. So-and-so lived alone in that house: her husband was a dentist and had left her for one of his patients. The single man in such-and-such cottage lost his wife to the teacher at drawing classes. The house at the end of the lane was vacant because its owner had hanged himself. The man in the old farm was on his sixth wife and no one was saying anything, but three of them had died. Suddenly, it didn't bode well, and we soon ran into trouble ourselves. We both had our separate frustrations and difficulties, and in retrospect, the truth was that we were summer stragglers who had attempted to prolong a holiday into a life. Areas of our relationship degenerated into farce.

Money was short and blame plentiful. We moved in on 7 May, 1997, the day of the General Election. The night before Hallowe'en, we had a bad row and I was thrown out.

It was ten o'clock. I walked back across the fields to the farm where Catherine and I had first met, Parker waddling behind me, and never spent another night with Pip or Polly.

I packed my books into an old Ford Sierra, bought for £300 from a man in Hereford, put Parker's basket in the back and returned to London. There I discovered that I had been cleaned out by a friend to whom I had lent my flat. It was all my own fault, but it was not a good situation and I was very grateful for the unconditional affection of my dog.

When you are down, the love of animals seems to have a purity that makes human love look confused and grounded in self-deception. Dogs don't have any ideas about love: they don't have any pictures of the sort of love-life they want, or of how they want to be perceived in that relationship. They don't gossip and don't boast or belittle. They don't save up small grievances until they feel rich in anger. They don't tell you shocking things about their parents or former partners but expect you to be nice to them all the same. They don't understand their own love, or rhapsodise about what love ought to be, or read romantic fiction or watch mainstream films. Their feelings seem unique, and truthful.

The fall-out was bad. For a few months I used to go back and stay on the farm, weaning myself off the place and people I loved. The two dogs missed each other badly and a curious thing used to happen. On arrival, Parker would go and sit outside the back door, and sniff the air. An hour or so later, Pip would appear, dashing through the farmyard, his red tongue hanging out, and the two of them would go off to the wild woods. I don't know how Pip knew Parker was there, but he always found him.

When Catherine and I weren't speaking, the dogs enforced some sort of relationship, as I was forever returning Pip to her. Unfortunately, we argued bitterly over the reasons for the break-up, and winning the argument became more important than telling the truth. With the exception of a week's house-sitting in the spring, I stopped going to Wales and it was a long time before the two Scotties saw each other again.

I had loved living in Wales and driving back to London, with the sun sinking behind me, felt grim. It would have been worse had I not had Parker. He had a sweet way of sitting on the front seat and resting his head on my left arm. It was comforting, though it made changing gear a little tricky.

2

When I came back to London with Parker he was eight months old, a small black tub with curly hair and a furiously whirring tail. He was used to being outside most of the day. Now, like other city dwellers, he had to take his pleasures in packets. Fortunately, he wasn't put out by the new life, so long as he had a strict routine of food and walks.

I discovered how I could use food tactically to make both our lives better. I began by feeding him once a day, as I'd always done, in the early evening. Now I realised that there were times he was bored, so I took to splitting his food, giving him half at lunchtime in the hope that he'd sleep for a bit. It worked for a while, then he discovered he was being diddled of play-time and I would feel his eyes boring holes in my back while I typed.

I had no escape from those eyes. He used to stare me down when I was eating, so I gave him the odd scrap, from which I discovered that he liked fish – kipper skins and sardines – best of all. From being a greedy pup, he became picky. There were lots of things he wouldn't eat: sweet things, bread, even salami. He preferred horrible, smelly things that were almost alive, that ran off the plate or had to be gnashed furiously, like old bits of cheese, and nasty old bones.

My flat in Islington was on the third floor of a block

built at the beginning of the 1960s. The outside was not pretty. The rendering was collapsing above the front door and the façade of the building was disfigured by dead window boxes.

In front of the block was a small, railed-off area of pavement, where wind-blown rubbish accumulated. The occupant of the ground-floor flat, Eddie, was wheelchair-bound and there was a worn wooden ramp leading up to the front door. Eddie was dismissive of his disability and always behaved like a man who just happened to have a wheelchair attached to him, but the ramp gave the block the feel of sheltered housing.

I used the larger of my two bedrooms as a study. The smaller one was taken up with a futon I bought in a rash moment. It's no secret that most futon-owners despise their purchases. Parker liked the futon, and my bedroom quickly became strewn with eviscerated squeaky toys – discarded once the squeak had been killed – and shredded novels.

I didn't care too much where he was kipping. I was too preoccupied with my desperate financial situation to impose rules. I was only envious that he knew, or thought he did, where his next dog-biscuit was coming from. From the back of the sofa in the sitting room, he could stare down into Popham Street, watching for passing dogs, or lazily eye the pigeons destroying my window boxes. When he heard other dogs, he would hop on his hind legs and instruct me to take him out. Sometimes if I refused he would take socks off the rack in the bedroom and chew them. One day, he peed in my left shoe. I called a shady hole under the table in the corner 'Sulking Corner', because that's where Parker would go when he thought I was cross – or when I hoovered.

He had always hated the Hoover. I suspect this stemmed from some trauma he suffered when he was a puppy. He regarded the Hoover as animate and would not go near it even when it was unplugged. It stood in the hall, next to the front door and he slunk past it fearfully. Once I saw him sniffing it, as if it was another dog, trying to work out which end was which.

There seemed to be a lot of confusing information about rearing dogs and I could not decide whether to take the Woodhouse way or opt for a less speciesist approach. In the end, I did what most do, and treated Parker like a peculiar child, with a mixture of intense affection and arbitrary regulation. I never actually thought of him as *my child* and felt slightly sick when people would ask my dog, 'How's your dad doing? Is he treating you well?' In spite of this, and my insistence that he was 'just a dog', I did come to think of him as my family. He needed me as a father even if I didn't want him as a son, and at that point, he seemed the closest to a child that I would ever have.

I took him everywhere. He was optimistic, regarding each new location as an opportunity for making friends and acquiring territory, sometimes both at the same time. He was still a novice at balancing on three legs, and if he sighted another dog while he was having a pee, he wobbled with excitement and all but fell over.

I hadn't counted on him making a stir. In Wales, no one gave a hoot about Scotties. Though originally bred for ratting (and, so I'm told, to snap at the heels of cattle), Scotties have long been regarded as more decorative than functional. In London, people stared and asked what he was. There were several things they used to say.

'Is that a black Westie?'

'Get a white one and you'll have a pair just like on the Black & White whisky bottle.'

'My mother always had Scotties.'

'We always had a Scottie when we were children.'

And: 'You don't see many of them nowadays.'

In those days of happy puppyhood, before he was bothered about who had been peeing on his lamp-post, Parker was universally welcoming. He trotted up to each stranger, tail twirling like a propeller, and had a wonderful way of using his ears to communicate, flattening them with shyness and pricking them up with curious interest.

Some people were afraid of black dogs and hurried away from him. Women in purdah would cross the road. Asian children were half-fascinated, half-frightened, and would run after Parker shouting, 'Boo!' in a welcoming sort of way.

He was excited by babies – squeaky, smiling creatures his own size – and they were fond of him. A friend with a small child once said that she had discovered in conversation with other mothers that one of the first words their children had spoken was 'doggy'.

'Look at the doggy,' mothers would say. 'What a funny little doggy.'

'Doggy. Mummy, Doggy.'

There were mothers with buggies who were wary of Parker, perhaps because they didn't know what he was. Inner-city horror stories about pit-bulls and Rottweilers going mad meant that these breeds were at least easily recognised. 'It's a Rottweiler, innit?' you'd hear one mother say to another, and they'd go their way unconcerned, because Rottweilers were part of their everyday lives, whereas a Scottie might be some new devil-dog.

Nearby lived an old Scottie called Max, clipped and

proper, with a stiff, quivering tail. His owner emerged from the Popham Estate at the end of the street each morning to walk to the newsagents. I never knew her name and I soon found out that this was the case with dog-owners. Within a few weeks I knew quite a few dogs: Ollie the Labrador and Baxter the fox-terrier and Henry the bull-mastiff without ever being on first-name terms with their owners. When we bumped into each other without our dogs we felt naked.

I felt I'd been away from London for a long time. I found it strange: huge, industrious, overcrowded and anonymous. In the six years I'd lived there I'd mostly dwelt amongst other middle-class types, and to be living now on the rough side of Islington was like stepping back in time. When I'd first come to London, I'd also stayed in a tiny council flat, just across the road from where I was living now – *and I'd hated dogs.*

In those days I worked at home, writing books about dictators, gangsters and murderous doctors. Outside, the estate was under attack from its inhabitants. Children dangled from the newly planted saplings; graffiti flourished and the communal areas went untended, deep in litter. I wanted excuses to escape outside but when I strolled along the pavements, or stood at street corners, I was aware that I had become another threatening feature in the landscape.

I saw my upstairs neighbour only once, when she knocked on the door demanding refuge from her ex who was going to 'feed her to the pigs in Totteridge'. Quivering with alcohol, she spent the night on the sofa and the next day walked past me without a flicker of recognition.

I came to hate city dogs. I hated the bowed, miscegenate

latch-key mutts that licked at the rubbish bags and piled dung on the pavements. I hated the frustrated, mad yapping of toy dogs, shut up all day. I was afraid of the Rottweilers slavering at the end of short chains, dragging overweight, pasty owners in their wake.

Autumn was a particular time for hating dogs, the greasy sycamore leaves concealing the filth they left on the pavements.

Dogs were part of country life and if I ever tried to imagine myself with a dog, it was in some remote, romantic, rural escape. Heaven knew what I'd be doing there and after a year in Wales I was to be none the wiser.

My parents had always had dogs and it was fine to walk them, but I'd never fancied the responsibility of looking after one. In any case, I assumed that people who had close relationships with animals had failed in the human arena.

I suppose that at bottom I was a little afraid of dogs. When I was three or four I was badly hurt when I spilled boiling coffee down my chest. I remember my mother pouring water from the kettle into the coffee pot, then going to answer the doorbell. My piggy little fingers reached up to clutch the pot and I ended up with a scab half an inch thick covering my front.

My parents had a collie called Angus. Laid up in bed for weeks, I remember my father joking that he was going to feed the scab to the dog.

I had nightmares about dogs. I dreamed I was being chased by huge Alsatians with red eyes and studded collars that were inside the house. I could hear their panting. I had to sleep with the bedroom door open and the landing light on. Long-toothed shadows fell through the doorway.

As I began to form opinions about adult relationships,

my fear of dogs re-emerged as a dread of couples-who-owned dogs. I saw all around me couples who could not talk about anything else, whose sole channel of communication was the dog.

No, I didn't fancy ending up as a dog-owner.

Living on that council estate in Islington in the early 1990s, I watched my surroundings fall to bits. The caretaker vanished. It was said that he was on paid sick-leave. After six months it was discovered that he had gone to fight as a mercenary in Bosnia.

In one of the ground-floor flats that opened onto the communal courtyard was a garrulous, bigoted ex-soldier in his sixties who had a daughter, confined to an electronic wheelchair.

The daughter had a little girl and the old soldier told me how the child was the offspring of a BT engineer who had 'banged up his daughter then done a runner'. She was dying and had largely lost her speech. Some afternoons, she would take her little girl out into the courtyard and watch her run around the smear of mud and twisted sticks that were all that was left of the landscaped playground.

One afternoon, I heard wailing. I looked out to see that the mother and daughter were outside and between them was a huge Alsatian. It looked uncertain as if it didn't know itself what it wanted, but it was intrigued by the fear of the small child. When it began to move towards her, the mother set off, her wheelchair whirring as she tried to catch up with the dog.

If the child ran, the dog padded after her; if she stopped, the dog would stop and wait. The mother whirred after them both, crying. The participants seemed helpless, even the dog. The prevailing atmosphere of fear dictated that it would all end badly.

It never occurred to me that I should actually do anything about it and I should think I wasn't the only one in that estate watching stupidly, unable to distinguish life from television. At last someone shouted and the dog seemed to wake up, jumped over a fence and vanished.

Shortly afterwards I moved north, to Upper Holloway, where I spent the idle hours watching dog-owners walk their mutts in the streets adjacent to Pentonville Prison. I hated the way they let their chained dogs crap, looking the other way, as if to disown them.

On weekends I used to go down into Camden. There were a lot of 'crusties' who hung around the Tube there, with mangy dogs on pieces of string, or beggars who used their dogs the way other beggars used children, thrusting their suffering in your face. These dogs lurched out from bundles of old clothes, Alsatian-Labrador mongrels, quite old most of them, with tottery thin legs and grey muzzles. They had names like 'Alfie' and 'Spike'.

London seemed full of threat to me, and dogs were part of the threat. I told everyone that the Chinese had it right, banning dogs altogether in cities.

Years later, all these objections turned out to be rather complex compared with the basic problem of having a dog in a town flat.

The smell.

'Scottie, isn't he?' said a tweedy chap in a deli. 'Great dogs. Greyfriars Bobby. Courageous, loyal. My mother had Scotties. But they stink like tin cans. Low-slung, you see.'

After the first few days Parker gave off a strong odour, both metallic and fungal. I have quite squalid tendencies and could mostly meet the dog halfway. I didn't mind the dribbles on the upholstery or his habit of burying biscuits down the back of the sofa. One's family do as much. But the smell gave me a bad headache. Using a thick green poison I had bought at a pet shop, I put on rubber gloves and washed him. The results were shocking. Because he was black and did not show the dirt, I had assumed Parker was clean. Instead, a stream of oily filth poured off him, consisting of soot and mud and small black pebbles caught up in his coat. Regular washings ensued. Parker hated being washed. At the sound of the shower – as of the Hoover – he would scuttle off to Sulking Corner.

Four or five times a day, I took Parker for walks round the surrounding area, along grand Georgian terraces and through the council estates. Islington's a muddle of rich and poor, and both sides seem proud of it. At night, I couldn't help but stare in through the windows of the big homes, where tastefully parted curtains showed off mirrors and chandeliers and rosewood veneer.

The other side of the street might be an estate, bright with yellow sodium light the colour of old beeswax, so that the walkways and staircases and doors and grilles looked like the fabric of a vast hive. The closer together people lived, the less they trusted each other and the more light they needed. Upper Street was lined with restaurants with puritanical interiors, catholic menus and hellish prices. On Saturdays, the theatre-going classes flocked to the Almeida to see Hollywood stars play the fringe.

My immediate neighbours lived for football, and I could tell when Arsenal had lost because the telephone booth at the end of the road was always smashed. When Arsenal did the double, the streets were ankle-deep in broken glass, the area was sealed off for the weekend and Upper Street was given over to a victory parade. Local kids grew up looking like footballs: short, white, and round, with cropped heads.

On hot nights people had furious rows, and the area echoed with obscenities. A man on the adjacent estate threw all his girlfriend's possessions out of the window – cooker, television, clothes – and crowned it all with a pot of blue paint before he was carted off to hospital.

There was a full-scale cockney funeral once: with plumed black horses in the street and ornate floral tributes, when the whole neighbourhood came out in respectful silence while the horses tossed their heads and the sun shone grey on the glass of the carriage, big as a royal coach.

Overweight single mothers bought fistfuls of lottery tickets from the local newsagent, where the grave Asian owner sat reading the *Economist* and selling the *Mirror*. There was little in his shop, besides packets of crisps, pink birthday cards, chocolate bars, cigarettes and dog food.

Before it opened in the mornings, a queue would form at the little chemist shop next door, of thin, pale, tattooed men and women. It was some time before I realised they weren't queuing for hairbrushes or toothpaste, but for methadone.

I was thoroughly middle class, but not so well off as others like me. Quite often I had £20 to last the week. Probably because of the shame of that relative poverty, the feeling of failure it brought, and the stubbornness it ingrained, I lost my sense of affinity with many of my old friends. On the other hand, my accent stood out in the local pub and I knew little about football, which was the common currency of chat. For some time, I went out little except to walk the dog, talking to other owners about the idiosyncrasies of our pets – what they ate, how they showed their displeasure, what they used to be like when they were younger.

Like my dog, I developed an interest in rubbish. There was so much of it about, and he regarded it all as important, lovingly re-marking old items and methodically incorporating the new ones into his daily rounds, whether a plastic bag or a discarded cooker. Some rubbish used to hang around for weeks; other objects moved slowly, as if caught up in a slow urban glacier or as if they were ripe enough to crawl. An old wooden-backed television set discarded at the bottom of Popham Street crept like a glass-backed tortoise, moving a little every night round to Britannia Row. Each day of its freedom, Parker greeted it as an old friend and peed on it affectionately. Eventually it was taken off to a dump.

I found Parker's interest strangely redemptive. Walls that were thick with tatters of posters and fragments of old tiles, crumbled rendering and splashes of graffiti were libraries for him, full of the smells of Islington dogs that had come and gone. His nose moved over the pavement like a bookworm on a grey page.

In January, defenestrated Christmas trees filled the pavement, creating dark pine forests into which Parker disappeared, just as he had done with the big forests in Wales.

I began to look at the pavement also. Occasionally, I came across beautiful things. The night of the first heavy frost of the year, I went out at five in the morning and found on the icy road a wedding bouquet, a bunch of artificial flowers, a thing of silk and lace and silver balls and red-wrapped sweets that seemed to have fallen from the winter sky.

I may have felt isolated, but whenever I was out and about with Parker, I was part of Dog-world. I used to think that there was some sort of demographic structure to Dog-world, that there were a lot of Labradors on Hampstead Heath and manicured toy-dogs – and the odd gentleman pervert like the Golden Retriever who assaulted my sister – in Kensington Gardens, while Primrose Hill drew in Bitzers ('bits 'er this and bits 'er that') from the surrounding estates, and spoiled pedigrees from Regent's Park Road.

The truth was more complex. Dog-world crossed age, sex and class. Dog-owners travelled from park to park and one was as likely to meet pedigrees in Clissold Park as in St James's Park. Clissold Park, in Labour-raddled Hackney, was the only one, I noticed, that offered free poo bags at the gates. Rich people adopted strays from Battersea, just as the less well off liked to splash out on their pets.

As my loathing of dog-shit had been one of the main reasons I had hated urban dogs, I became a manic pooper-scooper, my pockets stuffed full of plastic bags, scraping each fragment of Parker's waste from the grass. It wasn't easy. One twilight on Primrose Hill I found myself in the company of another walker, both of us stooped, moving slowly over the places where we had seen our dogs crouching. It was a fruitless search, but since we had seen each other begin to look, we were ashamed to give up. At last the other stood up straight and said, 'It can be awfully hard to find sometimes.'

Her honesty came too late. In desperation I had just bagged something hard and old and definitely nothing to do with me. I imagine I made her feel awful.

Slowly, I relaxed and began to enjoy the casual company of other dog-walkers. There was a delicate protocol to Dog-world. Encounters were controlled and finite. Walkers could disclose and be party to all sorts of intimacy – stories of hardship, of lost homes and broken families, childless marriages and lonely old age – so long as they talked about what happened to the dogs in the story. How this dog used to be part of a set-up with two dogs and the other dog was bigger, but the husband had lost his job because his back had given in and they'd lost the house and now they had a flat so the other dog had been sent away and the wife missed the other dog, and the other house, and she had to go to work full-time now so she couldn't walk even this dog as much as she liked. Oh – and they had children but they never heard from them, and that was the hardest thing of all. When the conversation reached a natural conclusion, we could take different paths, without any sense of disappointment. It was a co-operative confessional without any attitude of blame. Penance was built-in: the walk in the cold and the dark, but for the most part, there was no question of sin, only the search for consolation. People have dogs because there are too many of us and not enough love to go around.

Talking with a cab driver once I discovered that I was not alone in having felt uncomfortable in those days before I had Parker and wanted to walk after dark, but had no reason for being out on the streets. The cabbie had just lost his family dog, a retriever that had been put down. For years he had been used to walking the dog across a small neighbouring park, last thing at night. 'Now I scuttle across it,' he said. 'Without the dog, people must think I'm a pervert. I mean, what am I doing there – by myself?'

I suppose you could read all sorts of things into such a disclosure. On the whole, Londoners expect the worst of each other, and that makes them suspect the worst in themselves. The closer people squeeze for security, the more they look for a threat. The more people treat each other as freaks, the more they shape each other into the thing they fear.

Walking Parker I began to take a less suspicious view of others' behaviour, possibly because I felt I looked less like a threat. Walking behind that small black dog with his whirring tail and lolling pink tongue, I found myself rewarded by smiles and nods. If Parker hopped up and introduced himself to a stranger, they might walk off looking a bit less anonymous also. A puppy did what adult humans could not do for each other.

One day, I found myself over the other side of the Essex Road, by the estate where I had first lived when I came to London. Walking down the street came my former neighbour from upstairs, who had once spent a night on the sofa, cowering from her boyfriend, and had ignored me ever since.

She looked intact, so the Totteridge pigs never got fed, and she had with her two little girls – her daughters, I guess – dressed like her in lace, black leather and high heels.

'Look at that little dog,' she said to her girls. 'Innit sweet?' And six years after we had last spoken, she gave me a friendly smile, as if she'd seen me around somewhere before.

3

I needed money badly, but had no idea how I could earn a living wage without going back to journalism. For several years I'd worked for the *Daily Telegraph*, then accepted a lucrative contract from a Sunday newspaper, where I'd quickly become one of the numerous casualties of a surreal regime that had dragged dozens of dutiful hacks into the vortex of its professional suicide. I'd had a decent pay-off and ought to have put the experience behind me, but my confidence never recovered. I'd always wanted to write fiction, and this is what I'd been struggling at, all that time in Wales. After two years of dogged work, I had a mountain of debt and only a vague hope that I might be getting somewhere with my writing.

When I realised I was probably going to have to sell my flat, I remembered how happy I'd been at the *Telegraph* and begged its editor, Charles Moore, for work. Moore had warned me not to take the other job, but instead of saying 'Told you so,' he was interested in my frayed cuffs and asked me what I was up to. I muttered that I'd finished various short stories and there was some hope I'd have some published that year and he nodded politely. I knew it didn't sum up my life adequately, so I added that I lived alone with my dog, walked around a lot and had conversations with strange people.

His eyes lit up. 'One man and his dog wandering the

streets? It sounds what my children would call "sad".
Now, there's probably something in that.'

I went home, did a couple of dummy columns and
for a while heard nothing back.

Desperate for money, I took in a lodger – a Japanese
girl who was private and silent and stayed mostly in her
tiny bedroom. Something about this deference made
me also defer, so both of us kept to our quarters and
neither used the sitting room, which was left mostly to
Parker as a place to chew socks.

I also had an erratic source of income from my
brother John who would come and crash for the odd
night on my sofa. Afterwards I would rip off the cushions
and find pots of pound coins. Much of the time, though,
I found myself staring hungrily at Parker's dog-biscuits.

In March, Parker came up to his first birthday and
I blew £5 on two squeaky toys for him. One of them,
a cat, lasted about thirty seconds, and the other – a
ball – didn't interest him at all. Shortly afterwards, he
caught an ear infection. It had never occurred to me
that he might become ill and even though ear infections
– mostly caused by fleas or impacted wax – are common,
I was deeply distressed and felt even worse when the
vet said that there was a chance that one of Parker's
ear-drums had been perforated.

I blamed myself for it all. I thought the dog had
been carrying the burden of my wayward emotions
and his illness was a punishment. As any dog-owner
knows, it's horrible to see your pet in pain, as you
can't communicate to reassure them and don't know
how they experience and understand pain. Fortunately,
the infection cleared up after a course of antibiotics.

While at the vet I learned that there is a kind of dog-
tranquilliser which can be prescribed for a condition

known as 'separation anxiety', when dogs are badly affected by their owner's absence, chew everything in the house and pee everywhere. This drug is similar to the anti-depressants commonly prescribed to humans, which have only recently been licensed for use on animals.

I was intrigued by this. I thought it happened the other way round – that we experimented on animals before drugging ourselves – so this reversal of standard procedure might be seen as an unusually generous gesture towards our pets. On the other hand, I realised the drugs were probably first tried out on animals before being licensed for humans, so the depressive dog had never been far from the thoughts of the pharmaceutical companies.

It struck me that dog-tranquillisers were a leap forward in the way we impose our mental and emotional conditions on our pets. A sad dog might be the consequence of a neurotic owner, but it was obvious that many people found it easier to see and treat neurosis in their pet than in themselves.

Some people were frank about the way they used their pets. There was an Irishwoman who lived over the road – I didn't know her name – who had a small, hyperactive Pomeranian that looked like a toy collie. She never let this dog off the lead and as she walked forwards, very slowly, the dog ran round frantically in a circle until it had wound itself up off the pavement and all but throttled itself on the lead. Then it unwound the other way.

'He won't quieten down,' the woman said to me, apologising for the desperate excitement the Pomeranian showed on meeting Parker. 'I'm sorry, he's terrible. What am I to do with him?'

'He wants to play. Why don't you let him off the lead for a bit?'

'I couldn't do that. He'd be off.'

'How do you know until you try?'

'Now you sound like the dog-trainer . . .'

It turned out that she had taken her dog to behaviour classes but was too scared to follow any of the advice given. In the end she said glumly, but honestly, 'It's not the dog that's the problem: it's me. I'm too frightened. That's what the dog-trainer said.'

'If you know that, why can't you let the dog off his lead in a park?'

She shook her head sadly. 'I just can't. I haven't got it in me. I know it's me that's the problem. Do you think if I had him, you know, "done" it'd make a difference?' And off she went, dragging her twisting Pomeranian behind her, like a trailer for the main event.

I saw how I might allow anxieties I transposed onto the dog to be reflected back on me, and to shape my life. I had to remember that Parker was just a dog. I had my own problems, and he had his.

To my great relief, the *Telegraph* took up the column. I marked this new beginning by replanting my window boxes, which had been destroyed by pigeons, and found what I thought was a dead bird lying among the shrivelled stalks. When I reached out to pick it up and throw it away, the pigeon opened one pink eye and hopped aside to show me that it was sitting on two dirty white eggs, laid on a nest of twigs and sweet-wrappers.

Parker took to sitting next to the window, his nose pressed to the glass, staring curiously at the nesting pigeon: it stared back at him and blinked slowly.

I wished I was still in the Borders, walking up the

River Wye. Instead, I was next to the Essex Road, a rusty stream of traffic, trickier than a river, with a hundred currents moving at different speeds. Parker hated the Essex Road, and particularly the 38 bus, that rumbles down through Islington to the West End. At the sight of the bus he flattened himself against the wall. The explosion of its hydraulic brakes terrified him.

On our side of the Essex Road was one of his favourite spots, Steve Hatt's the fishmonger. Just behind the shop was a small car park, full of old fish-ice where Parker was in the gutter and in heaven at the same time.

Hell lay across the road in the shape of a taxidermist's called Get Stuffed. Parker would not go near the shop, and if we had to walk past he thrashed wildly on his lead. In the windows were dead birds, a lion, a bear, a stuffed collie. One night, Parker was so engrossed in some wayward trail that he stumbled right into the door of the shop. Though it was locked and barred, he could still see the dim outlines of dead animals and set up a fierce, frightened barking, hopping away as if he'd just been stung by a bee.

When I met the owner as he was opening up once, I told him that my dog hated his store. 'They all do,' he said, not without satisfaction, 'cos they think they're going to end up here.'

Some of Parker's uncomplaining, puppy-charm vanished along with his puppy fat. Soon after we moved back to Town, he'd made friends with Audrey and Molly, who worked in Lockey's Coal Shop just off the Essex Road. During the winter months, the door was open all day to customers and their dogs, and the two women kept a supply of dog biscuits somewhere in the back, that they doled out to passing mutts.

As a pup, Parker had run up to Audrey and Molly

wagging furiously, his tail spinning first one way, then the other. He crunched his way through the biscuits he was offered, asked for more and returned every bit of attention five-fold. After his first birthday, his mind began to wander. He took the attention for granted and was forever trying to cock his leg on their stacks of smokeless coal.

'Give us a wag, Parkie. No wags?' Audrey would say. 'Oh dear, look at him. He's got his own little ways now.'

He had indeed got 'his own little ways'. Most of these were terrier traits. Dogs' characters are so much determined by breeding that once you've owned a pedigree you find yourself taking a sceptical view of the psychological origins of animal behaviour, believing instead that it's all down to genes.

The foremost characteristic of terriers is their lack of self-knowledge: they are small dogs who imagine they are big and have to spend much of their lives learning about their true size.

The first dog I saw Parker challenge was a vast hairy Japanese thing. I'd just assured the owner that my dog was still a puppy and friendly, but he took one sniff of the other and leapt at him. Fortunately, there was a fence between them that prevented the other dog from swallowing him like a piece of sushi. Its owner complimented me on Parker's aggression. 'He's got to learn to look after himself,' he said. It was true, but sad that Parker wouldn't be able any more to win all his battles with just a wagging tail.

I quickly learned the signs to watch out for: the tail that beat to a tense aerial and the right paw, raised slowly from the ground and twitching, like a hesitating gunslinger. Parker's confidence in any impending battle could be measured by the degree of twitch. Sometimes the paw would go up, then down, and he would back off, and sometimes the paw seemed afflicted by the palsy before he leaped at the other dog's neck.

He never developed any fighting skills. Bred for ratting, his one attacking move was to try and seize the other dog by the scruff of the neck and shake it to pieces, which was hopeless when his opponent was two feet taller than him. Other dogs don't care what they get hold of.

He also became intrigued by sex. Scotties are notoriously bad breeders and for a long time, Parker didn't so much as roger a chair leg. However, his nose gave him great pleasure. Once Parker had worked out that girls smelled good, nothing would stop him. I saw the first signs of his obsession on Primrose Hill where he came across two Yorkshire terriers, wisps of silky fur that looked more like fly-fishing lures than dogs. They were being walked by a massive Mancunian builder called Mickey, who said their names were Chica and Gigi.

'My girlfriend named them,' he explained. 'Chica's, like, something Spanish and Gigi, like in the film, "thank 'eavens for little girls."'

Parker agreed with that. One of the dogs was lying on her back while he sniffed her intently.

'Don't worry. She's been on heat,' said Mickey.

Just then, a Frenchwoman passed by with a Bedlington terrier that became similarly entranced. Its owner erupted with contempt.

'She is a naughty girl to lie like that,' she said. 'She is shameless.'

'She's being crafty,' Mickey explained. 'So long as she's on her back, see, they can't get her.'

'Non. She is a naughty girl. I never seen such a

naughty girl. You can stop a dog running after a girl but not if she is such a naughty one.'

The Mancunian shrugged his shoulders. Who was he to object to a woman defending male nature? When he tried to take his dogs away, Parker followed, and the rest of our walk was a disaster. I would put Parker on the leash and lead him away to some other part of Primrose Hill. When I let him off, he would straightaway run off in pursuit of the Yorkies, both of which eventually escaped his nose by running up their owner's leg and sitting on his shoulders.

Parker began to mark a lot more. Spring afternoons in London parks became full of potential embarrassment, as he tried to cock his leg on dozing picnickers. He even peed on the foot of an American jogger who paused momentarily in Kensington Gardens. The American took it as such a personal comment that he was too ashamed to pursue the matter with me, but wandered off, shaking his head, demoralised.

On Primrose Hill we met an Asian woman with a Labrador that she introduced as 'Clintoon's dog'. I didn't have the wit to respond that mine had belonged to Roosevelt.

'Does your dog have bark?' she asked. 'Ugly bark or beautiful bark?'

I had not thought about a bark being beautiful, but it is true that some dogs have nobler barks than others. Parker, generally quiet like most Scotties, had developed a deep bark, comical in that it was several times larger than himself, that he used as a means to introduce himself at a distance. He would become agitated if other dogs remained indifferent. There was only one thing worse than not being noticed, which was being noticed by all the other dogs at the same time. When a pack came streaming across the field in response to his challenge, he hid behind my legs and made grumpy, sniffling noises.

For a long time, I thought that what Parker wanted above all else was a special dog-friend to replace Pip, who we had left behind in Wales. There were several Islington dogs who were friends, on and off. Baxter the old fox-terrier in the launderette up the road, who used to be trundled out of his basket to meet Parker. There was a Labrador who lived in a ground-floor council flat in Popham Street who was very nice as a pup, but his owner worked for Rentokil and was always off in his Rentokil van, leaving the dog alone and under-exercised. The dog began to dig huge holes in the tiny back garden and quickly became fat and nasty. Then there was Toast, a fierce Border collie whose owner lodged in a tiny room in a flat down the road, along with seven cats. That didn't work out either.

We followed several false trails before I had to admit that true friends aren't easily replaced, and that the quality of company is as much to do with environment as personality. Moreover, Parker was whimsical in his likes and dislikes and became more so: one moment he might seem very keen on another dog and play delightedly with it, the next moment, his nose would catch some other scent among the grass, and he would wander off, quite forgetting his play-pal.

One dog he was always pleased to see was Lola, a white terrier mongrel we came across sitting outside a restaurant in Colebrook Row, near Islington Green. As it turned out, her owner Tony Maroni – a Portobello-born Italian – ran the restaurant and didn't object to me bringing Parker inside.

This was good news. It had proved hard to find a pub or café where I could take the dog. Even the dingiest dives, knee-deep in fag ash and beer had signs on their doors forbidding dogs, and it added to my sense of persecution that the signs were mostly silhouettes of Scotties with a bloody red slash through them. I was once refused admission by a landlord on the grounds that he didn't like Scotties because – yet again – his mother always had one of those, and he hated them. Generally there was no explanation given. Most first-class cricket is said to be played in front of one man and a dog, but this is a lie. I tried and failed to get Parker into the Oval and Lords.

I assumed there was some EEC regulation forbidding dogs in bars and restaurants, but Tony told me that provided the animals didn't go in the kitchen, there was no legal bar. It depended on the owner.

I used to stop off at Tony's for coffee when we were out walking. It was a friendly place and Tony and his mother always spoiled Parker. Tony, a delightful man who looked a bit like a handsome dragon with toothache, made howling noises, which worked Lola up into a frenzy of excitement and she and Parker would chase each other round and round the tables.

Once or twice I took Parker there in the evenings, too. He tended to be a bit forward with the other customers, though none seemed to mind. One evening a youngish man sat there by himself, pecking miserably at a solitary meal, looking as if he'd been stood up. Parker hopped into the seat opposite, put his head on the table, and stared across fondly.

'Bring another glass,' said the man, delighted. 'My date's arrived after all.'

The income from the *Telegraph* wasn't sufficient. Serious

debt doesn't respond to small injections of cash: it requires excision. It became clear that I would have to sell my flat, but I held out in hope and tried to live in the place as if I was going to be there for a while. I wanted to make it more comfortable. Periodically I made plans for improving the flat, but in the end the furthest I went was to take up the carpets and this only because they were old, thin and grey; the rubber underlay had perished and the dust that came up from them made me cough badly. Afterwards, when I sat at my desk with my back to the door, I could hear Parker's claws clicking over the bare boards. I didn't have to turn around to know that his nose was poking around the corner of my door and his eyes were boring holes in my back.

'Not yet,' I would say. 'Let me finish this. In five minutes.'

After a pause, the feet would click away and I would hear a thump as he hopped back onto the sofa to continue his surveillance of the pigeons.

I often lied to Parker about when he would next be taken for a walk and became self-conscious about this duplicity, convinced that he could sense a contradiction between the certainty in my voice, and the plain fact that he was not being taken for a walk. Sometimes he would come and ask twice in quick succession as if to be sure that he was gauging my response correctly, or to see whether I could be influenced if not by argument, then by persistence.

I wondered whether Parker could tell that I was lying. I wondered if *he'd* learn to lie. I'd always understood that lying was a peculiarly human characteristic: it was saying the thing-that-is-not. It was partly because dogs were dumb animals that some people considered them more pure emotionally than ourselves, as if our ability to speak

had disrupted the immediacy of our feelings so that
even when we were not being deliberately untruthful,
language had created traps into which humans fell,
clichés and plots, generalisations and silly absolutes.

One old friend I still saw regularly was Belle who lived
on the other side of London, up the north end of
Notting Hill. On weekends I sometimes took Parker
over there for a change of scenery. Belle veered between
'frivolity' as she called it, in that she liked reading *Vogue*,
buying girlie clothes and being invited to parties, and a
chilling psychological seriousness, fed by learned works
– particularly those of Carl Jung – that she would fillet
for quotes to substantiate her opinions of others. She
advocated naked self-knowledge, in others, and could see
straight through the cunning device of Parker.

'You and that dog,' she said sternly, brushing Parker
from her lap. 'That dog is cosseted. You project your
ego onto that dog.'

I pointed out that she frequently told me that I had
serious problems and was a deeply unhappy person – 'a
dark person'. But the dog was a happy dog. If I was so
bloody miserable, why was Parker so full of beans?

She had a ready answer. 'The dog is a face for you. The
dog is happy, because you are concealing your shadow
behind it. I tell you, for your own salvation, you must
get rid of that dog.'

It was true that I did hide behind Parker in the sense
that I used him as an excuse to be elsewhere and as
a social front. But I had very good reasons for being
down in the dumps and didn't feel I was naturally a
misery. From my scrappy knowledge of psychoanalysis
I believed that Belle's view of me was a projection of her
own true inner night, because when she wasn't telling

me what was wrong with me, she was mythologising her own emotional travails in a rather too-splendid light. Sometimes I remembered her lectures and was very irritated, then I'd think about her and laugh, because she had a huge heart and irresistible charm, and could be very funny, and she did look a bit like Catherine Deneuve.

I'd known her for years, but it was only after I'd returned to London that I saw her regularly. I began to look forward to seeing her and sometimes wondered if perhaps we might be better than friends. More than anything, I wanted in any partner that they should be an ally, first and foremost, and I thought that Belle and I did fundamentally know and like each other. Mutual friends advised me that I was being encouraged by her. I didn't force it, I didn't even think about it too seriously, but I still received a stinging slap across the concealed ego when she rejected the advances I had not yet made.

Personally I believe that it was the bone that put her off. On the Portobello Road I bought a large marrow bone – 'that fossil' she called it – for Parker. She was horrified to see it disappear into my bag to be taken home and shortly afterwards, as if this meaty purchase had bought into the focus the physical potential of our relationship, she threw cold water over me, warning me not to get the wrong idea about our cosy chats. Sadly, this rejection re-awoke in me the need for a human as opposed to a doggy relationship. Belle was not happy when shortly afterwards I fell for her friend Maud, a beautiful but restless Kensington butterfly, pleased to be prized by me but frankly, more comfortable when she was thought common.

All this trickiness provoked an eruption of neglected emotions and all at once my heart was pumping the colours of teenage love – purple, gold, blue and very grey. Perhaps I'd never really been a teenager: perhaps this was teen spirit, fifteen years delayed by public school, Oxford and the fake maturity of the premature responsibilities I had subsequently assumed. Perhaps it was necessary. I had to grow up, and I couldn't do that without being childish again. It didn't drag me down: I was flying. I was high on life. I ran with Parker across the scrappy wastes of North London, woofing my delight. 'Yip yip,' we went together, running off to the wild woods.

Somewhere in the middle of this business, the three of us – four including Mr P – spent a strange weekend together in Shropshire at Combermere Abbey. I had been invited there by a pair of dogs or rather, Parker had been invited. As a consequence of the column he was now receiving a steady stream of correspondence from other dogs, and Echo and Zulu, a Labrador and flat-coated retriever, wrote from Combermere to offer Parker an estate cottage for a weekend, on condition that he helped eliminate the rabbit problem on the estate. I had to accompany Parker, and so I invited Belle and Maud.

When we arrived at Combermere I thought there was a mistake. I had expected a cottage with cramped bedrooms, nylon stretch-cover sofas and an electric fire that smelled of burning hair. Instead we had the entire wing of an old stone courtyard, two kitchens, three bathrooms and at least four double bedrooms. There were linen sheets, open fires and the fridges were full of cakes. It was too much after life in the Islington dog basket. Overwhelmed, Parker and I passed the first night huddled under my jacket in the corner of the sitting room.

Outside lay more grandeur; hundreds of acres of woodland and a great silver lake on which the sun set like Excalibur sinking into the water. We stared, open-mouthed: Parker ran a flag up his tail, raised his head, sniffed the air like a charger spoiling for battle and shot off at a gallop. Overtaken by this medieval splendour, he became a questing knight, Sir Parkalot du Lac, and for the next three days he went diligently about the business of pursuing rabbits, questing here and questing there, and always just in front of him, the white bob of his disappearing foe.

Belle spent most of the weekend trying out the various sofas, complaining of stomach-ache and fatigue, and watching grimly while Maud and I flirted.

We went swimming in the lake. The water was icy cold, with a mist of midges in the shallows, and sucking green weed underfoot. Further out, the water was warmer in the late sun. We decided to follow some swans along the track of the sunset to the other side of the lake, elope and never go back to London. But among the reeds sat Sir Parkalot, waiting, unable to continue his quest without us.

For three days, Sir Parkalot quested without success. The only prize he bore off was a pig's ear I bought him in Nantwich, which he buried in one of the immaculate flowerbeds, although he did flush out a camp of Boy Scouts, surprising their chief in the latrine.

My pursuit of Maud also turned into a fiasco. She told me that I had won her heart, but added that it was a long way from Ladbroke Grove, where she lived, to Islington. On the one occasion she made the trip, 'It took almost an hour.' I didn't realise that she was being serious, that West Londoners regard the rest of the world as pointless and inaccessible.

And that was that. She was to call me to confirm a date. I waited for six weeks for her call, then decided that this was an excruciating foolishness to round off a horrible year. I had indeed become a sad chap with a dog, and though I remained sure that deep down I was a happy person, it seemed as if my involvement with Belle's world had made me into what she had insisted I was: a misery.

I worked out that the problem was that these women really liked 'boys', and try as might, I could never be a boy. I was barking up the wrong tree. I felt an idiot. I decided never again to make a fool of myself in love.

I was brooding over this down by the Regent's canal in Islington when I met a bedraggled Scotsman who turned out to be a struggling writer. He was queer and forty-something, and exercising a tubby old pooch that belonged to him and his boyfriend.

He had a nervous stutter and kind eyes behind his glasses, but his collar was filthy and his breath smelled of whisky though it was early in the morning. He was working, he said, on the biography of a thriller writer, a lesbian, who had recently died. For some reason, he began telling me about her habit of falling hopelessly in love with unsuitable girls. He said that she had told him that she knew they might not care for her, and might take advantage of her, but whatever she gave them it was nothing to that which the giving gave her.

'Auden told Benjamin Britten,' he said – as much to himself as me – 'that no one can hope to progress as a human being until they have hurt or been hurt in love.'

I found this reassuring. I scored highly on both counts, so I ought soon to acquire a rare level of human development. I never saw the chap again.

The bone I had bought for Parker on the Portobello Road disappeared into his basket and after a bit, I forgot altogether about it.

That strip of the Regents Canal is very pretty. On dog-day afternoons, Parker liked to rootle down there, where a cool, clean Islington was reflected beneath the painted barges. There was a line of trees where dogs met and touched noses in the shade. At either end of the tow-path were gates, and I once narrowly escaped being locked in at twilight. The man from the council was supposed to arrive one end, lock the gate then walk the path to ensure he wasn't locking anybody in, before exiting at the other gate and securing it behind him. Instead, he would peer quickly down the path, lock the gate, then drive round to the other end. He was just locking the second gate as I came up the steps: he was embarrassed when he saw me and my dog and muttered about council economies, and how he had to lock up so many properties now.

It was a very upside-down time. At one point spring turned to winter without an intermission. It was snowing when the pigeon eggs in my window box hatched out. I saw it happen: flakes were settling on the edge of the nest as a pink thing, all elbows and neck, fought its way out into the snow. The parents sat a little way off, similarly amazed. For a day or two, the mother sat on the nest, through rain and sleet. One morning she was gone: the newly hatched pigeon was dead, and the other egg still unbroken. The crows cleaned the nest within hours.

In May, I knew I couldn't stave off my creditors any more, and so I put my flat on the market. I calculated that it would be two or three years before I was again in a position to buy, and decided to rent for a while. As a temporary measure, I asked my friend Max if I could stay in his house in Notting Hill.

Max was rich and had a huge house, an air-conditioned spaceship, hidden away behind the ecclesiastical façade of a redundant church called St Jude's. It had five ensuite bedrooms, a laundry room, pool-room and a small garden. The various levels were connected with spiral staircases, many of which led through false walls and bookcases back to the master bedroom. With an interior decorated in New York bachelor chic, it felt a little like a cross between the *Starship Enterprise* and a contemporary version of Castle Dracula.

Max was generous and long-suffering when it came to guests. I had stayed there for two weeks before, when builders had removed the roof from a flat I had in Marylebone. Other guests had been known to linger for years. There had generally been a Cohu knocking about the place. My sister, Lucy, had once gone to stay there for a few weeks and remained for more than twelve months. Max didn't flinch when I asked him.

'Well, there's Percy and Adèle and possibly Jeremy staying,' he said, 'but it's always jolly nice to have a Cohu too. I may have to leave to make room for you all. As it happens, I think I've probably got some work in America in the summer.'

Max had a dog also, a boxer called Charlie, a good-natured but rather dim specimen. When Parker was a puppy the two had got along fine. Charlie was a loyal hound, and rescued Lucy when that golden retriever tried to mount her in Kensington Gardens, attacking the other dog without hesitation. (Parker, then about six months old, hopped up and down woofing furiously.) One of the conditions of my staying was that the two dogs could co-exist. Neither had been neutered, so it was potentially tricky. Even as we discussed the arrival of Parker, Charlie put on his most poignant face, offered Max a paw and shot my dog a look of bitter jealousy. Parker sniffed his privates shiftily.

We went off to Suffolk for a couple of days, to Max's parents, taking both dogs 'for a bit of bonding'. It all went well until Parker and Sophie set eyes on each other.

Sophie, a corgi, had been recently acquired by Max's parents and was a ravishing little thing with great big eyes and a coat a mixture of chocolate and vanilla. Unfortunately, she was on heat and took a shine to Parker, who was beside himself with excitement.

Sophie yapped for his attention. When Parker wagged his way towards his beloved, Charlie went for him with real venom. Thereafter, Parker lay outside the kitchen door, gazing longingly at his corgi sweetheart, who yapped endearments at him across the supine, sulking body of the boxer.

Most of the weekend Sophie was in a cage in the corner of the kitchen, watched over by Max's mother, who squirted her with a water pistol each time she barked. For ten dazzling minutes, Sophie gave her warder the slip and in the garden danced the Seven Veils for Parker. Parker, however, got no further than playing kiss-chase. This was just as well, as a Corgi–Scottie cross would mingle one of the noisiest breeds with one of the most stubborn.

The second night, I forestalled any conflict by setting up my tent in the garden. This Baden-Powell approach took Parker's mind off girls and turned him back to healthy things like chasing squirrels and rolling in sheep-dung.

After a bit, with Sophie locked back in a cage, the

two boys got on perfectly well, leading Max to observe that, 'It was just a chick thing,' and they'd be fine together, much to my relief as we now had temporary accommodation.

Max's mother carried on squirting Sophie with the ray-gun water-pistol, purchased at a village fête. 'It's what the vet told me to do,' she said. 'When she starts flirting, I squirt her.'

The dog didn't stop barking, but added a twitch in anticipation of punishment.

'You can see how I was brought up,' said Max, sadly.

4

Priced for a quick sale, my flat was soon snapped up by a young couple. Completion was scheduled for the end of July. In the meantime there was little for me to do but watch Parker's tail as he dawdled through the streets of Islington. Sometimes the tail went from half-mast to upright cavalry flag when he sighted another dog, but that was the limit of excitement on those summer afternoons.

On hot days he plodded so slowly I almost fell asleep behind him. He dawdled, yawning, from the base of one tree to the next like an old man strolling from café to café.

One day I looked up and saw that he had emerged from the scratty jungle of crisp packets and beer cans at the base of a tree with chewing gum on his paws and a fag-butt dangling from his whiskers. He sat at the entrance to the flats, looking like Andy Capp. This was true Urban Dog.

An etiolated Irishman weaving homewards stopped, gave him a pat and jokingly asked him for a smoke.

'What a lovely feller,' he said to me. 'What a lovely little feller.' And with that, he dropped his trousers to show me that, in the absence of Ireland in the World Cup, he was wearing tartan underwear in support of the surviving celtic side.

There was something about the movement of football

on-screen that intrigued Parker, and he watched a bit of the World Cup, sitting on my shoulder on the sofa, fag in mouth. He could not distinguish between shouts of enthusiasm and of rage: when Owen scored against Argentina he fled in terror to hide in the bathroom. The Final did little for him: he spent most of it scratching an elusive flea. Later, he was to develop a horror of the game after a traumatic incident in a park, but that was some months off.

One day he was enjoying a leisurely sniff at a kerbstone in a very tidy street, when he was verbally assaulted by one of the residents.

'Oi, you. Get out of it, you filthy creature,' shouted a short, elderly woman with frizzed white hair. 'Yer dirty creature. Off with you.'

Parker looked quizzically at her. I told her he wasn't doing anything. She gestured up and down the street. 'Don't want no filthy creature leaving its packet here.'

I waved a plastic bag at her. From her horrified reaction I might have taken out a packet of condoms. It was as if she had understood from Parker's sniffing that there was something filthy-juicy on her street. After a few more witchy curses at Parker – who carried on regardless, sniffing away – she turned and continued yacking to her friend, also white-haired. They fizzed away like two Alka-Seltzers in a glass.

You can't stop a dog sniffing and Scotties live through their noses. As the weather became warm, so the sniffs became richer. Parker seemed to scrutinise each and every smell, to note, record, and follow invisible trails along pavements, zigzagging crazily, licking lamp-posts and dribbling with excitement at old street corners. He seemed to be high on the smells; he almost levitated on them. The smells were mostly other dogs' 'packets'. Translated to human terms, I suppose that made him a frightful gossip.

He hated being washed. I used to speak to him in a special psychopathic voice to lure him out of hiding: 'Come on, Parkie. It's all right. Just a little washie-washie,' I cooed. When he saw the rubber gloves going on, he would flee, with a very serious expression on his face. In his terms, I was committing a grave error.

Friends said that he would smell less if I had him 'done', but quite apart from being sqeamish about the operation and the effect it might have on his character, I feared from experience that it might create particular problems for me. One of Parker's favourite dogs was Gus, a trim 'done' Westie who wagged like clockwork and was walked around the block at about the same time as we went on sniff-patrol. They wagged away at each other and Parker sniffed Gus and as some kind of confused reaction to Gus's neutered state, Parker inevitably cocked his leg on the foot of Gus's owner. To be fair, he only managed to hit her once and she was understanding. 'He's not the first,' she said, laughing like a drain. Her stockings were ruined.

As summer wore on, Parker had a bad bout of fleas. At night he scratched furiously and I had to expel him from my bedroom. I bought flea-spray, and reading the instructions was shocked to realise that if Parker had fleas, the whole of my flat was infested and had to be sprayed. There were fleas in my blankets, clothes and towels, in the sofa and in all the dark holes where he liked to hide.

I tried all sorts of flea-poisons. Occasionally, I thought I could hear the fleas bouncing up and down, packing their flea-bags and moving, but they didn't go far, only to new corners of the flat. It became apparent that these were genetically mutant super-fleas, to whom the poisons were manna, even the toxic green sludge that I had been assured killed everything. As a last gasp, I tried a flea collar, which seemed to work, though it looked a touch seedy and clerical. It proved, though, to be a public stigma.

'Stay away from that dog,' I heard one mother say to her child. 'Can't you see he's got fleas?'

I knew a haircut would help. I'd put it off for as long as I could, and I'd left Parker untrimmed, shaggy and shapeless, a kind of indeterminate dog, recognisable to dog-aficionados as an unkempt Scottie: lovable to some because of his rug of wild hair, but also a source of pain to those Scottie purists who used to write to the *Telegraph* and ask that Parker 'please, please, be smartened up'.

The fleas loved Parker's long coat just as much as I did so I bit the bullet and booked him in with a dog-groomer. There was a six-week waiting list. It hadn't occurred to me that there would be such a demand for dog-grooming.

I used to get my own hair cut at George's on the Essex Road, where the owner offered to help me out.

'It's something I've often thought of,' he said. 'There's money in dogs. Cost you between twenty and forty quid to get him done. I could do that. I could give him a number two for six-fifty. I've got the clippers. I could have a hair-cutting superstore. "We do you *and* your pet". 'Spose I'd have to go on a course, though. And you've got to do their bums.'

One morning, feeling a bit of a sneaky heel, I took Parker down the Essex Road to a salon called Furry Tales. He suspected nothing, even when we were inside the store, where he found a stone dog under one of the seats and spent five minutes trying to elicit some response from it. When Clea the groomer clocked in, she turned out to be kind and pretty and Parker immediately hopped up and gave her a big kiss.

'Oh, you lovely boy,' she said. 'You special boy. We're going to get on famously.'

Parker trotted off with her, backstage, his tail wagging. 'Come back at eleven,' she said, over her shoulder.

I felt a lurch in my stomach as I watched Parker's bottom waddle off into the sunset. I didn't like the idea of leaving him. I've seen dogs being groomed, standing under blow-dryers: some sang and some howled. It wasn't quite an Oliver Stone film, but none seemed very happy.

When I went back to Furry Tales I had to ring down to the grooming cubicle and under Clea's voice I heard a dryer and a dog howling above it. It sounded like a canine torture chamber: I imagined dogs hung up on a washing line. He'd be up in five minutes, Clea said, and I had an awful picture of them gluing bits of his fur back on.

The dog that came back into the room wasn't the Parker I had known, but a handsome Scottie with a colonel's whiskers and big bat ears and the body of a cuddly black rhino. When he saw me, he waved his paws just the same as before, and I realised it was Parker after all, but Parker with the child's clothes off.

'He was very good,' said Clea. 'He doesn't mind you doing things to him.'

He gave her another kiss when they said goodbye, and all my horrid fears about groomers were dispelled. I took the new Parker off for a test-run on Hampstead Heath, where he ran and leapt and growled ferociously at the funny men, who sat in the shade waiting for God knows what. Parker loved being a Scottie.

Occasionally I felt as if I was going up the walls while I waited to quit my small flat, and as summer arrived, I took to keeping my tent in the boot of my car. At weekends I would chuck Parker in the back and get out of town. We went to Dorset, and camped near Lulworth Cove, walking up and down the vast white waves of the cliffs in the early morning before the crowds arrived, then going inland, stumbling into a secret overgrown valley dotted with crumbling brick farm buildings. Not far away was an army range: birds were singing and butterflies drifting among the cow parsley while a mile or so away, grenades popped off like corks.

Another weekend we went to the South Downs, outside Brighton, and camped under the Black Windmill. The farmer who owned the fields was in a state of shock. Not long before, he'd had a beef herd, but he'd had to slaughter all his cattle during the BSE crisis. Now he had, he said, 'a herd of campers'. He said we were welcome to walk where we wanted. There were two or three adjacent meadows he had mown, where he used to keep his cattle. 'I just cut them down so they look all right,' he said.

That weekend was very warm, and the sky was filled with sea-haze. Parker cantered across the downs, and devoted some time to stalking a Westie with whom we crossed paths. Ahead of us walked a couple with a pair of Labradors. Every time their dogs crapped, the couple would stop and go through a lengthy procedure, unpacking bags from a rucksack, bagging up the excrement and putting it carefully inside the backpack. My head filled with strange thoughts about what they were going to do when they got home.

Parker liked camping out, although he wasn't a very good companion in a tent, and thought nothing of stealing my bedding. He liked to sit outside and growl at the night. Campsites were good for meeting other dogs.

From time to time, we did stay in a house. In Berkshire – a good county for dogs – we stayed in a pretty cottage with old friends. They had two small boys, who were fascinated by Parker, and wanted him to participate in their happy children's games.

I watched them creep up on him as he lay on the lawn, twitching in his sleep. Perhaps he was reliving his days in Wales and how he used to play with his old dog-friend Pip. He squeaked, 'Yip! Yip! Yip Grrr! Ruff! Ruff!' as his dreams took him into the dark Welsh woods, running after a rabbit, brambles tearing at his coat and dead twigs sticking to his bottom. And perhaps, down in the woods, from among the silent stands of pine and the piles of moulted needles, came another streak of blackness with an echo to his yipping. It was Pip, with whom he had spent such happy times hunting! Together they raced out into the sunlit fields to frolic in the bluebells, bobbing up and down like black porpoises among blue waves, rolling in the new grass, their eyes glowing amber with happiness.

Then a strange, menacing rattling noise woke Parker up. He was not in Wales. He was in a Berkshire back garden and standing over him was Tom, a five-year-old wearing a sheriff's uniform.

'Put handcuffs on dog,' said Sheriff Tom grimly, rattling the same, 'and take him to jail.'

Tom's father intervened. 'Now now,' he said. 'That's

not how you get friendly with a dog. Be gentle with him. Stroke him.'

'I want a dog,' said Tom's mother, 'but *he* won't let us,' pointing to her husband. 'Why won't you let us have one?'

'I don't know,' mused the father. 'Possibly because they're rather dirty. Except Parker, of course, who's exceptionally fragrant. Then again, we don't want to end up as one of those families who only talk about the dog, do we?'

Tom was not altogether sure what a dog was. His desire to harness and imprison Parker originated partly in a knowledge of ponies and partly because he was obsessed with *The Wind in the Willows* and in particular, the incarceration of Mr Toad. More than anything, Parker struck him as a good toad-substitute.

Under his father's tutelage, Sheriff Tom began to stroke Parker but, as matters were progressing nicely, along came little Robin, Tom's three-year-old brother, clutching a length of bamboo.

'Fish!' he yelled at Parker, who scuttled away to hide under a garden bench.

On the whole, Parker liked children. But large numbers of them proved a hairy business, like the crowds of kids that assembled for their pre-school fags outside the local comprehensive in Islington.

They would begin by saying, 'Nice doggie,' but quickly the stroking would turn to patting and the patting to pulling as they began to parody their affection.

There was no threat of such violence from Sheriff Tom, but the jail had been constructed in the pantry from chairs and cushions and it had to be filled by something. It looked rather chilly and the only food on offer was a stick of Lego.

Sheriff Tom would not be put off the trail and stalked Parker most of the weekend, jingling his handcuffs, as we crossed the border into Hampshire and fled along the chalky downs in stultifying heat.

'Jail,' he said, crying with frustration.

In the end, Tom's father decided that he would have to do the honourable thing. He sighed deeply.

'I suppose *I'll* have to play Toad,' he said.

Half an hour later, I looked up from my book to see Tom's father – a highly respected man in his profession – sneak past wearing a pinny with a tea-towel over his head.

'What on earth are you doing?' asked his wife.

'Toad escaped from jail dressed as a washerwoman,' he replied defiantly. His son got the point immediately and was at last distracted from his pursuit of Parker to run after Daddy.

This all made perfect sense to Tom's mother. 'That's the real reason we're not allowed any pets,' she confided 'It's because he wouldn't be the centre of attention. And he wouldn't get the chance to dress up.'

It wasn't always possible to escape London, and weekends in Town were enlivened by the antics of my downstairs neighbours, Philip and Joe, a couple of good-natured lads, mad-for it and very often out-of-it, with an astonishing tolerance of chemicals. They played a lot of loud music – drum and bass, Italian opera and Radiohead – and on Friday nights their flat would host a rolling party.

Sometimes the stairwell filled with drunk friends who had penetrated the communal door but couldn't get into the flat, because one or both of their hosts had passed out. I used to hand out blankets to the refugees.

Once I came back late to see three figures swarming up the front block, trying to get in through the windows of the flat, as if an SAS raid was in progress.

Joe could sleep through anything, particularly after a few drinks, but Philip was twitchier and more chemically deranged. Short, but gangling with very long arms, cropped hair, sunken eyes and a menacing intelligence, he reminded me of one of the droogs in *A Clockwork Orange*. Essentially good-natured, he was prone to sudden bouts of paranoia, which he afterwards regretted.

After I took up my carpets, the sound of Parker's claws could be clearly heard downstairs.

'It sounds like he's on a skateboard,' said Philip, 'It's like, here we go, Will's putting on his roller skates and taking Parker for a spin.'

A few nights later Philip came bashing on my door at two in the morning in his dressing gown. He looked like he'd been having a terrible time.

'Will you stop moving the f****** furniture,' he shouted. 'I'm not a w****** but the next time I come up, you'll know.'

'Know what?' I asked, half-asleep.

'You'll know then,' he said grimly. 'Hello, Parker,' he added politely, as the dog stuck a curious nose round the door.

'You'll know,' he repeated over his shoulder as he went down the stairs.

I couldn't decide whether I should take this vague threat seriously, and was puzzled by his insistence that I had been 'moving furniture'. Eventually I decided that Philip had gone from mad-for-it to mad-because-of-it.

A few nights later more or less the same thing happened. Philip came to my door in his dressing gown, gaunt and mad, accusing me of moving furniture. I asked him to come in and look around. He got the point.

'You haven't got any furniture,' he said, bewildered. 'Sorry, mate. It must be in my head.' He departed, apologetic and perplexed and I went back to bed, feeling pretty smug.

Later I was wakened by an eerie noise. It was a rumble, then a thud followed by another, as if a skeleton had popped up through the floorboards and was dragging itself towards my bed. It did indeed sound as if someone was dragging furniture around. I got up to investigate and saw in the sitting room, lit by a crack of sick summer moonlight, Parker gnashing furiously at the pale old bone I had bought him on the Portobello. He must have been hiding it somewhere and disinterring it for night-time snacking. On the bare boards this made a terrible racket and it probably sounded much worse in the flat beneath.

I said nothing about this to my poor neighbour, who went to the doctor for prescription tablets and turned up at my door, bottle in hand, apologising and saying that he now couldn't hear a thing. I nodded: it had probably been that *fin-de-siècle* psychosis they all talked about.

Then he produced a present for my dog, and I sighed. It was a massive marrow-bone.

'Philip,' I said, 'Parker has a confession to make . . .'

5

Moving from Islington was a pretty straightforward business. I didn't have much in the way of furniture, just the excruciatingly uncomfortable futon, a sofa-bed – ruined by my dog – and an over-size television set that I bought when I had an unemployed friend staying in my flat who I thought needed something to do during the day. In the event he preferred to amuse himself by dialling a wide selection of premium rate phone-lines.

I did have miles of books and it took three days of swearing and sweating to pack them all into boxes. One by one Parker's hiding places disappeared until the flat was empty except for his bowl and my desk – an Ikea slab much defaced by scribblings of the 'why oh why' variety. Parker hunched miserably in a corner, trying to conceal himself behind a roll of bubble-wrap.

Most of my stuff was going to a lock-up in Shepherds Bush. I called Gary, the removal man who had moved me in and asked him to move me out. He had moved me to Wales too. 'You must have a strange view of people's lives,' I said, embarrassed. 'You don't see them from year to year, think they're getting on fine, then they call you and ask you to cart them off to another fresh start.'

As an Australian, he confined his reply to, 'Ah well, ain't life a bitch. We'll be round Monday.'

It took him and a burly sidekick about forty minutes

to empty my flat, and two hours later, my possessions were in a 25-foot metal cage, among the rows of other lives in limbo. As I padlocked the door and walked away from my past life, I felt the hand of liberty reach out and take me.

It wasn't quite that easy, however. I'd had to make the move a couple of days before contracts were exchanged, so Parker and I spent two more nights in the bare flat. I'd also become so used to things not quite working out that I was convinced the sale would fall through. When the couple who were buying the place began to lay claim to curtains and cookers that weren't included in the price, I just gave them away. There was also a question about the bit of wasteland behind the flats, as to whether the freehold was properly incorporated. It had once been a garden, then had been covered with asphalt. Roses and elder had grown through this, turning it into one of those fragrant bits of wild urban wasteland that wouldn't be half so nice if the tenants were remotely responsible. The roses were a marvel; huge, heavy and blood-red. They had petals that felt like soft skin and a warm, sleepy scent that lingered for days after they were cut.

We left Islington on a hot, dusty day in July. I took Parker round to say goodbye to his dog-friends and he had a last sniff around the back of Steve Hatt's fish shop. Then I walked up and down the empty flat, poking at the ghosts that huddled naked in the corners. I experienced all the usual niggles that people suffer when leaving a home peremptorily. Why had I never painted the hall or re-tiled the bathroom? And I'd had that idea – a good one – of knocking the big bedroom and the sitting room together, maybe taking in the kitchen too. What a wide, light space that would have been! But it all took money and money was why I was selling up.

At four-thirty, my solicitor called to say that the money was in my bank. I unplugged the phone. Parker was already waiting at the door: there was nothing for him here any more, just dusty floorboards. I'd locked up and was about to drop the keys through the door when I remembered to take my car-keys off the bunch. I felt a twinge of panic as I separated them. We were homeless.

Not really, of course. Not in the way that thousands are really homeless, having to doss in doorways or beg shelter from a local authority. We had a luxurious temporary home at Max's house in Notting Hill, a palace by anyone's standards. It had been a struggle in the latter months in the Islington dog basket: all the plumbing was beginning to give up the ghost and the flat, as if sensing our departure, began to shed paint and dirt like an old skin. In Notting Hill there would be baths and showers and washing machines and dryers and clean linen. It would be clean and so would we. I would sleep in the Garden Room at Max's and each morning I'd be able to throw open the doors onto the little suntrap of vines and rustic furniture and let Parker out to sniff around the arboretum. By the time we reached Notting Hill I'd psyched myself into a state of optimistic bliss which was unaffected when the door to St Jude's was answered by Percy.

I knew Percy would be staying there, but I'd no idea that Max had already left the country, leaving Percy in charge of the house. Percy and I got on well, but it meant that there would be no governor-by-right of the property. It's always a problem when there are a mass of guests but no host. Percy was a well-known but shy artist, who lived abroad most of the time and stayed at Max's when he had to visit England to be fêted, something that happened more frequently as the years passed. He was much older than Max, and divorced, and his sagacious, vulpine looks clouded over when he saw too many women around. Much of the time he sat thinking, bundled self-consciously in a white towelling dressing gown, of which there was a vast supply at St Jude's. He did not like his routines disturbed and though gentle and sympathetic by inclination, he would become crotchety if he felt his creative space was being invaded by indelicate hooves.

Percy was delighted to see Parker, and for the first few minutes addressed all his remarks to me through my dog, as if he was some sort of medium. He explained that he'd hoped to place us in the Garden Room, but this had been taken by a woman – pronounced 'woe-man' – called Adèle, an old girlfriend of Max's who was staying while her roof was repaired.

'To be honest, Parker,' he wheezed, shaking the dog by the paw, 'I don't care for her too much. She's very bossy. And she drinks. And she smokes. None of which I can do any more. And she obviously thinks I'm a silly old fool in a dressing gown. I have this feeling she's plotting. You watch what you put in the fridge because someone – and I'm not saying who – is rifling the supplies.'

By reason of seniority, not to say achievement, Percy had the best room, a self-contained flat with a kitchenette and enough room for him to work. The other desirable billet, the Tobacco Suite, was occupied by the fourth guest, Jeremy, so Parker and I were left with the Film Star Suite, otherwise known as the Edgar Allan Poe Room. This was bad news. Situated in the former crypt of

St Jude's, the Film Star Suite was a windowless triangular cabin. Like the rest of the house, it was opulently fitted out, with leather-covered doors and hand-printed wallpaper, but it could feel like a luxurious padded cell.

One positive aspect of Max's absence was that his dog Charlie had been sent off to the country. Parker had the run of the place, and any number of dog baskets to lounge in. On the other hand, I had forgotten that the various floors of the house were connected by steep spiral staircases, which proved too much for the short legs of the Scottie. He was fine going up, but squeaked with panic at the downhill view. As I was unloading the car, I lost contact with my dog, and traced his yelps to a pool of shadow in the cavernous living room where he had just been trodden on by Percy.

'Poor Parker,' said Percy, mortified at the pain he'd caused. I explained that Parker found it hard to follow me around because of the spiral staircases. Percy shook his head; his huge, sad eyes swept over Parker like weepy moons over a black hill. 'Then how will he get outside to the garden to have a tinkle?' he asked me.

Here was something I hadn't considered. One of the advantages of having a garden was that Mr P would be able to go and attend to some of his daily business without my participation. Direct access was available to the garden only via a twisty staircase with a flap at the bottom. It was possible to go down an orthodox staircase, but this presented a choice of routes at the bottom, either through the Garden Room or the study.

'I don't know,' I said to Percy. 'I imagine I'll have to teach him to go through the study.'

Percy transferred his melancholy eyes to me. 'I think it would be far simpler,' he said softly, 'if you were to permit me to give him a few little spiral staircase lessons.'

Transfixed, I nodded my half-assent, thinking that no one would really want to teach a Scottie how to walk down a staircase. Percy suddenly lifted his head. 'Is that rain?' he asked me. 'Do you hear rain? Come quickly. To the kitchen. Now.'

He took me gently but firmly by the arm and led me into the dazzling chrome-plated circular kitchen, where a spiky jungle of pristine kitchen implements dangled at head-height. Pushing these to one side, Percy pointed to the ceiling, where two open skylights disclosed a grey, humid London afternoon. There was a distant rumble of thunder. As the first heavy drops of water fell, a red sensor blinked in the ceiling, a motor started up, and the skylights began slowly to close of their own accord.

Percy watched, a look of serene calm settling on his face as the descending glass turned the heavy sky a coffee tint. He sighed, contented when the windows hissed tight into their frames.

'Seal all exits,' he murmured. 'Prepare to launch ship.'

We had arrived on planet Notting Hill.

St Jude's *was* rather like a spaceship. When the door clicked shut, you left behind the traffic and sunlight for a cool dark world of unvarying climate, that glowed dully with polished maple and red leather. The air-conditioning and humidifying systems hummed like engines, and during the night an ice-machine made a ghostly clanking, churning out buckets of cubes. Entry was controlled by video-screens: the linen was collected and delivered and a company could also bring in food. There was no reason ever to go out.

Yet at some level, the old church was resistant to its new use and longed to return to its original form of a large, damp hall. Walls would sag into underground spaces, springs flowed up through the stone flags and fresh paint would be discoloured by rain that had seeped through the numerous windows. There were always builders at work, and for many of them the place had become a home from home. They even brought their children along for the day. The contractor had become a good friend of Max's and had all but married one long-term house guest. St Jude's was a family business.

Parker was thrilled with the green little garden out the back, and went sniffing the ivy and growling at the neighbouring cats. Halfway up a tree in the garden was a grey plastic squirrel that I knew Max was inordinately fond of, because he'd discovered it lying in the street. He always found things in the street, mostly money. He found pound coins where others found pennies. Though rich, he had long given up his vices. He had a strong puritanical streak, nurtured in the days when he had lived in a bedsit on a diet of tinned pilchards. His first love was for music, but he'd discovered he had a gift for writing film scripts. The work wasn't too bad, he said, if you could get sacked after the first draft. Despite his intelligence, he adored whimsical objects, like the squirrel, and had an enthusiastically morbid streak.

When we were sort of settled in, I took Parker for a walk and bumped into Adèle sitting outside a neighbouring Greek restaurant with a man she introduced as 'a business associate', lashing into a bottle of filthy red wine. She was a tough, attractive publisher, who enjoyed a 'good wind-up'. She gave me a friendly glower and invited me to share another bottle of acid.

'Have you seen Percy yet?' she asked. 'What's his

problem? He's not exactly matey.' She explained that he exuded a glacial chill whenever she met him. She'd ceded the entire top of the house to him and never dared put her head 'above decks'. I said that Percy was a private chap and there was some sort of territorial dispute going on. 'He's shy and sensitive, like you,' I said, but Adèle wasn't the flirty sort.

'He cooks all the time,' she sneered. 'He's always fussing over some exquisite little meal. Oh, and the smells!' She wasn't interested in food and only went to restaurants because other people insisted on eating while they drank. She said that Percy had been stealing her milk. I told her that he believed the same about her. 'I suppose it is possible there might be another thief about,' she said. 'Jeremy is in the house, too, but he's a drinker.'

I said I didn't know Jeremy very well. He was a journalist friend of Max's from university days. 'Oh, well he knows *you* well, he says,' she informed me. 'He knows you and your dog,' she sniggered, her lip curling as if it had been snagged by a fish-hook. 'You should hear him talk about that dog. Incidentally, are you still writing that stuff? I could write your column,' she said. 'I could do that easily. Pah.'

She explained to her friend that I was 'the dog man' from the newspaper. Her companion was a thin, crumpled, middle-aged man from some distant province. 'Dogs! I'll tell you a story about dogs,' he said grimly. 'It was our cairn terrier that killed my father. He came home with too much whisky in him and trod on the dog, which scratched him. He caught tetanus and was dead in days.'

'Good God,' I said, 'what an awful story. What happened to the dog?'

'People always ask that,' he said, with a wry smile. 'People always ask what happened to the dog. Obviously, one wouldn't feel the same way about it afterwards.'

'That's just human nature,' said Adèle, 'to be more interested in killers rather than their victims. We know what happened to the victims. They died.'

The man wouldn't elaborate. The terrier had probably been done for manslaughter, and the penalty for this is to be given away, as opposed to being put down. The punishments meted out to pets tend to be serious, because they can't express repentance. You can't forgive a creature that doesn't know it's done anything wrong.

'There's Jeremy,' said Adèle suddenly and waved at a stick-thin figure dressed in funeral black, who was trailing a cane-handled umbrella along the opposite pavement. He didn't look at all well. He favoured a style that evoked an English version of William Burroughs, a sort of high-Tory turned junkie, dressing in the reactionary chic of Savile Row suits with specially crafted pockets for his 'stash'. Now the image had become the man. He was only a couple of years older than me, but his jaw was protruding like a fist, his skin was a horrible yellow pallor and his cough sounded like a hammer on his thin chest. He shook my hand and winced.

'So butch,' he murmured. 'All that dog-handling.'

'Jeremy was being frightfully funny about your column the other day,' said Adèle. 'Said it gave off a strongly non-heterosexual odour.'

Jeremy hummed and haahed. 'I didn't quite put it that way,' he said. 'I did say something about, you know, only in England could one write about a doggy-woggy.' He looked down at Parker with a livid grin. 'Nice doggy,' he said. 'Woof woof.'

'He's just jealous – and he's not feeling on top of

things,' Adèle whispered to me. 'He's very worried about Clinton.'

'What's up with Clinton?'

'My income,' coughed Jeremy. 'I've got this deal where I do an anti-Clinton column. I've been demanding he be impeached for years. Now it looks like it's going to happen for sure and I realise I've just shafted myself. He's been worth two grand a month to me.'

'I've a good idea. You could get a dog and write about it,' said Adèle. 'By the way, did you try that place I recommended?'

'Oh yes,' he said. 'Amazing. From what I remember.'

'You found it?' said Adèle. 'You did? That's good. I told him to go to this cool drinking-hole I found,' she explained to me, with a delighted wink. 'It's called Crash and it's covered inside with pictures of fatalities in famous car crashes. It's up behind Westbourne Park. The front is discreet, but inside . . .'

'It's a blast,' said Jeremy, giving me the look of a veteran cop for a hopeless rookie. He lit a cigarette, striking a match with one hand, without removing it from the book. I saw that he had burned his forefinger and struggled to conceal the pain. I had to stop myself from telling him to go and run it under a tap.

As I said, Adèle liked a wind-up and this sounded as if Jeremy was being had. It was a good gag, as Jeremy prided himself as a connoisseur of debauchery and if it sounded nasty, he must find it.

'You really went there?' asked Adèle, looking pleased with herself. 'Oh, what joy.' She patted Parker happily. 'I miss my dog,' she said. 'Had to send her away while the roof's being done.'

I had forgotten that she was a dog-owner. She had a standard poodle.

It was a good gag, but when I looked at Jeremy, I saw he was a sick man. Suddenly I wanted to go. I excused myself, and hitched up Parker.

Adèle shook her head. 'Always walking that dog. My dog gets walked once a week. Don't spoil them. Keep 'em keen, keep 'em mean.'

'You wouldn't have much to write about,' I said.

I spent my first night at Max's in a puddle of wine. I didn't have to worry about money or accommodation, but I was miserable as sin. I realised I had become so used to having a supportive network of anxieties that without them I felt as empty-handed as I had done the previous autumn, when I walked away from the house I shared in Wales, across the fields one night, with Parker waddling behind me.

Among the books I had brought with me was *Desperate Journeys, Abandoned Souls*, by Edward Leslie, a collection of stories of castaways, shipwrecks and marooned sailors. Dipping into it, I noticed that some survivors found the process of merely living as hard to adjust to as their more forlorn circumstances had been.

When Alexander Selkirk – Defoe's model for Robinson Crusoe – was rescued, his reaction was unexpected. 'The man frequently bewailed his return to the world,' observed one writer, 'which could not, he said, with all its enjoyments, restore him to the tranquillity of his solitude.'

I couldn't decide whether I had been shipwrecked or rescued. I passed out and woke up on a sand-coloured sofa, under a vast domed sky of a ceiling. Parker was prowling round and round the house, trying to find some small corner to settle in. I wished I was some-where else, anywhere: France or Spain, or Ireland, but

I couldn't take Parker to France or Spain and bring him back. I could take him to Ireland. Perhaps we could settle there, in some bungalow out on the West Coast, watching the Atlantic crash against the shore and the moss crawl up the walls.

I settled on taking Parker round the block. At the end of our smart road of white villas was a hostel full of young Spaniards who had spilled out onto the pavements and were having an impromptu party, their sibilant accents making the street strange as Seville. Further over, on the corner of Ladbroke Square there was another hostel, for Czech students, and from that came the gloomy sound of piano music in a darkened room.

We were lost in some odd space that crammed Andalusia against Eastern Europe. Parker was fine. As a castaway, he was first-rate in improving his circumstances. He straight away set about carving out a piece of territory, marking lamp-posts, and doorways, sniffing out potential rivals and possible flirts. The streets of Kensington and Chelsea were blank paper to him, waiting for his signature. I couldn't imitate him to the letter, but a bit of his optimism rubbed off on me. It would be a home, like other homes. And one day, there would be a home of our own.

Later, I found another bit in Edward Leslie's book in which he observes that some survivors deal with chaotic situations by imposing over themselves 'a rigid and, on the face of it, slightly absurd order. It is as if they expected to stave off madness and disaster by regimentation'. Walking the dog can be a bit like that.

One of the problems I had with moving to Notting Hill was that I'd sneered at the smugness of some West Londoners, their obsession with fashion and brittle celebrity. They seemed to be pretty humourless too, very much into the bulimic drama of their own lives. Of course, this was a generalisation, as I realised the moment I moved there and became one of them.

I can't excuse the fact that at first I liked Notting Hill, particularly the Portobello Road, early on sunny mornings while they were still scraping yesterday off the streets. It had a dazed, hung-over feeling to it, the colours of the shops scratched and creased like old record sleeves. As we walked north up to Golborne Road it was like swimming out from a sedate poolside into a raffish sea clogged with old fish-heads. Parker found juicy patches under the flyover on the Portobello and plenty of Moroccan scraps on the Golborne Road.

We were only ten minutes from Kensington Gardens, too, where there were dogs with names like Chloë and Miranda, and tourists who asked if they could take Parker's photograph. He had become a sight, just like Kensington Palace. Most knew he was a Scottie, but sometimes when they asked, 'What kind of dog is that?' I'd make up breeds. 'It's an Iranian towzer,' I'd say, or a 'Himalayan poncho.'

Within a few days I calmed down and instead of running away altogether, settled on taking Parker to Ireland for a holiday. I hadn't had a proper holiday for years. With a dog, accommodation would be a problem, so I thought we'd camp out and as part of my plans I went looking for an old Landrover. I'd always wanted one: it would go anywhere, and we could always sleep in it.

I eventually found one advertised in *Loot*, an old Series III shortwheel base with a hard-top. It was being sold by Brian from Plaistow, a burly affable man who lived in a house perched precariously on a mountain of car spares.

He whizzed the heavy old car around the East End as if it were a motor-bike.

'I dunno,' he sighed. 'Some cars, you put yourself into them, and suddenly they're gone. This'll be handy for parking in the West End; you can nudge the other cars about.'

He was so attached to the car he agreed to sell it to me only after I'd been out for a meal with friends and family. At some point in the evening I realised that it was his son's birthday but the boy hadn't turned up, so I had been sandwiched between the husband and wife to fill the empty spot. I was a stray human, handy to have around.

I said I'd be back in a couple of days to pick up the car. My old Ford Sierra, the colour and shape of a wedge of green cheese, filled with the dust of Wales, fag-ash and hairs of the dog, was disposed of. Adèle offered to buy it for a nominal sum, as her vintage Porsche, like her house, was in pieces. She took it to be checked at a garage, where it was declared a death trap. The mechanic marvelled that it had lasted so long. It was a faithful old horse, but alas there was no pasture for it but the scrapyard.

Percy said that he'd be happy to look after Parker for the odd day, but I didn't want to impose. When I had had to go away for work and couldn't take Parker, I put him in with a dog-sitter for two nights. She had long pink-painted nails and lived in Primrose Hill in a flat full of dogs and oval-framed photographs of dogs. Parker peed the moment he arrived. She didn't mind that but, when I went to pick him up, she told me she couldn't have him again. He had quarrelled with another guest of hers who belonged to a local dignitary, and her social standing meant she couldn't rule in Parker's favour.

'Poor Parker! I could look after him,' said Percy, when I told him the story. 'I'd like to do that. We could crack on with those spiral staircase lessons.'

'Oh yes,' I said.

His manner became suspiciously casual. 'By the way, do you know where Max bought that grey squirrel in the garden?'

'He found it. I really don't know where you'd buy one.'

'Oh dear oh dear. I caught it with my sleeve and knocked it off. It's broken.'

'I shouldn't think it matters. Hang on – maybe it does. Max has a thing about that squirrel.'

'That's it. That's it. He has a thing. And the worst is that Adèle was in the Garden Room and I'm sure she saw me do it. It was an accident, but what if she tells Max? What am I to do? She'll say the most frightful things about me.'

I said that we hadn't heard a squeak from Max for weeks, and Adèle was due to move out shortly. She'd forget, and Max would never know. After that, I helped him glue the squirrel back together.

When I went back to Plaistow to collect my Landrover, Brian had read my column and there was a look of disbelief in his pebbly eyes.

'It was twee,' he said, filling in the vehicle transfer document. 'A bit camp. Who'd of thought it from a big, hairy bloke like you?'

Brian was definitely a geezer. In the yard, his Alsatian was barking. He showed me where it had bitten him the day before. I thought of the two genteel ladies who had stopped me and Parker on the street that morning, of the dog-owners who write to

Parker, enclosing photographs and sweet stories of their Scotties. I could see that the column might not be Brian's cup of char.

'What's your surname,' he asked, 'for the form?'

'Twee,' I said. 'Will Twee.'

Brian was fishing around in his yard, looking for the 'sticks' for the soft-top on my new car, when he came across a cardboard box.

'Oh,' he said, clapping his hand to his forehead. 'It's the pigeon. It's dead. We found a pigeon that seemed a bit ill, so we put it in here with a bit of food.' He called to his wife that the pigeon had passed away.

So much for twee. Even I know that there's nothing you can do for a sick London yard-bird except wring its neck.

Brian and I stayed in touch for a while. He was a charmer, but I could see he had an evil side too. He invited me and Parker up to Essex to a weekend cottage he had, where he used to hide from his wife and family. I was a bit wary, but I was on a voyage out and felt obliged to follow up the encounter.

It was a sad place, by a bleak main road, shuttered and dirty and packed to the roof with junk he'd collected. He was a hoarder. There were bottles of vintage wine shoved into every drawer and cupboard, and jumbo bags of crisps alongside valuable first editions and crates of condensed milk. We went for a walk around a neighbouring reservoir, a drab overgrown place where I kept thinking Parker would stumble on the dismembered body of one of Brian's associates. After a nightmarish pub crawl, we sat up drinking until morning, when he told me all about his neighbour, 'the stuck-up bitch' and suggested that we round off the night by popping over the fence and throttling some of her livestock. Perhaps he was joking, but his blue eyes were very dead. I began to feel a little nervous and left early. I still liked him, but I excused myself from further invitations.

Adèle used to rag me about how I 'sat on the fence'. The advantage of my ambivalence was that I could help everybody get on with everybody else. I was an expert survivor. Despite the coolness between Adèle and Percy, life at St Jude's maintained a reasonably happy order, with each one of us taking on a self-appointed task. Percy collected money for the cleaner, Adèle stacked the dishwasher and ensured that the snooker table was perfectly level. I was in charge of the garden, and Jeremy of drinking, though Adèle disputed that assertion.

Percy repeated his offer of dog-sitting, and one day I took him up on it while I went off for lunch. When I came back I caught Percy at it. He had Parker seated at the top of a set of spiral stairs, and was talking to him in a gentle but firm voice. 'Now, come on Parker,' he said, looming over the little dog with an odd smile on his face. 'You have to take these little spiral staircase lessons seriously. We'll try it one more time. I'm going to help you, but don't make me impatient. Now what is that waving paw all about?'

'It means anxiety,' I said, interrupting. 'One paw means he's worried. A squeak means he's very worried.' Parker squeaked and ran gratefully to me. Percy turned pinkish.

'We were just having a little lesson,' he said. 'He has to know how to get down the spiral staircases, or he won't be able to get to the garden to have a tinkle when he wants one.'

'He can go the long way round.'

Percy shrugged. 'He'll get lost. I'm sorry our little

lessons have to stop,' he said to Parker. 'A day will come when my efforts will be appreciated.'

At last Max called and left a message saying that he was in Los Angeles, working, but he was fairly hopeful he was going to be sacked soon. He needed his old Amstrad word-processor and was going to come back for it. Adèle wasn't at all pleased to hear this. The work on her flat was going slowly and she needed to stay on for a couple more weeks.

'Percy will bitch about me to Max,' she said, holding a cold glass of vodka to her temples. 'He'll blame me for the fag-butts lying around, which are mostly Jeremy's, and the empties, at least half of which are yours.'

I said that Percy was convinced she'd seen him breaking the squirrel in the garden. Her face shattered with laughter. 'So it *was* him! I didn't say anything because I thought it might be you, as you're so weird about animals. I couldn't work out whether I was suffering from vodka vision. I saw a figure in a white dressing gown, about seven in the morning, talking to the bloody squirrel. Then there was some shouting and he ran off.'

Remembering the spiral staircase lessons I wondered what Percy had been teaching the squirrel. I told Adèle I was sure that she and Percy could get on if they'd only sit down and talk. 'You both know that it's Jeremy who pilfers your stuff,' I said. I remembered something Max had said about Jeremy, how he was somebody whose presence you generally felt as an absence, an empty unmade bed or a missing pint of milk – one of those guests.

'Of course it's not really that,' she said. 'I never seriously thought Percy was a pilferer. The problem is that we've never been formally introduced. It's Max's fault. If he were here he could sit us down together.'

'You could arrange a discussion,' I said. 'You could ask him out for a meal.'

'He doesn't drink,' she said despondently, reluctant to relinquish her animosity.

'He used to,' I said. 'He used to drink like a fish. It's just that he can't do it now.'

She digested this and nodded. Percy had gone up her estimation. 'Can't is different from won't,' she said fairly. 'Maybe there'll be an opening.'

A few days later, we were walking to the vet when Parker was attacked on the Talbot Road by a massive green-striped cat. He hadn't seen his assailant coming and was shaken by the experience.

'Rough area,' murmured the vet. 'Cat-muggings are common.' He was giving Parker some booster shots and a health check-up. 'He's in pretty good shape,' he commented. 'Doesn't even have fleas.'

The vet then showed me how to test for fleas, brushing the fur on the back of the dog's neck onto a piece of kitchen roll, then dabbing the black bits that came off with a damp piece of cotton wool. If the wool turned red, it indicated the presence of droppings, which were 'just dried blood'. The fleas had plagued Parker throughout our time in Islington, but it looked as if we'd given them the slip.

An hour or so after visiting the vet's, Parker went belly-up on the floor, so groggy that he could not be roused even by a piece of bacon waved in front of his nose. I rang the vet, who told me it was just the shots, but he'd be out for a bit. I'd been planning to go and complete the shopping for our holiday in Ireland, but Parker wasn't moving. Reluctantly, I decided to ask

Percy to look after him and found the artist in the
kitchen, experimenting with something that smelled
like orange goulash. He said he'd keep an eye on
Parker. 'No, no,' he said, not looking up. 'Before you
say it, I won't give him any more staircase lessons.'

There was a lot of shopping to do: a spare tent,
sleeping bags, a stove, food and batteries. We would
be prepared for anything. It was a hot, humid day,
threatening rain, the traffic was bad and I didn't get
back until after six. Parker didn't come to the door
when I walked in, and didn't come when I called him.
For a moment, my heart sank as I imagined the scenario
that had played out in my absence. How Percy, unable to
shake off his disciplinary tic, had frog-marched Parker
off some sheer ledge. Hearing voices, I traced Percy to
the kitchen where, to my surprise, I found him seated
with Adèle, who was watching raptly as the rain hissed
down and the electronic windows closed.

'Hello, old boy,' said Adèle. 'Would you like a vodka?
Have you seen these windows? I never knew. Until today
I'd never been up here. Too bad about your dog.'

'Naughty Will,' said Percy, shaking his finger at me.
'Naughty Will.'

'What is going on? Where's Parker?'

'I told you – you should have let me teach him how
to use the spiral staircase,' said Percy.

I was becoming agitated and demanded to know
what they had done with Parker. Percy gently took
Adèle's glass from her hand and gave it an apprecia-
tive sniff.

Adèle poured herself another bumper. 'Parker is in
the dog-house. He's hiding under the snooker table.
Nothing to worry about. It's all cleaned up now.'

'He couldn't get into the garden,' hissed Percy. 'So

he went into the Garden Room. If the lessons had continued . . .' Their heads wagged in unison.

'Quite disgusting,' said Adèle. 'I was furious at the time, but Percy calmed me down. He explained that it wasn't really Parker's fault.'

I gathered that, unable to find his way into the garden, Parker had done something horrible in Adèle's room. But his habits were pretty regular, so the accident must have been provoked. It might have been the shots, I thought, and was about to apologise when in a corner of the kitchen I glimpsed a piece of crucial evidence the conspirators had overlooked: Parker's bowl. It contained a large puddle of dark gravy. I picked it up and sniffed. There was a strong citrus odour.

'Percy, what were you cooking? Orange goulash or something? You didn't give him any, did you?'

Percy shifted his bulk a fraction and coughed. 'Just a taste. He asked me.'

I waved the bowl at Adèle. 'I'm sorry,' I said, 'but you realise that the reason Parker did something in your room was Percy's poisonous cooking.'

She examined her nails: she didn't have any nails. She lit another cigarette. 'He is your dog,' she said, 'and your responsibility. Moreover, chum, from what I can gather, you prevented Percy from teaching Parker how to get into the garden.' She stared unflinching at me. The pair of them had settled their differences at my expense. You ought to be pleased, her look seemed to say. Shut up.

'I don't suppose this has anything to do with a broken squirrel?' I asked.

'That?' said Adèle. 'Oh, we don't know who broke that. But we think there can only have been one suspect. Dogs chase squirrels. But don't worry, my dear fellow. We won't say a thing.'

'Mum's the word,' promised Percy. 'Dear old mum's the word. If only the lessons had continued.'

When Max returned one afternoon, I was packing and the floor of his office was covered with army surplus tents and sacks. 'Where on earth are you going?' he asked. 'The Central African Republic?'

'Ireland.'

'They do have shops there, you know,' he muttered. 'The Irish are pretty good about that sort of thing. They have hotels too, and roads.' He eyed the multi-pack of dog food incredulously. 'They may even have some of that,' he said. He gave me a present, a mug decorated with a Scottie dog, and took a stroll around his home. 'Everything looks fine,' he said. 'And how is Percy getting on with Adèle?'

'Never better. It turns out they're both dog-lovers.'

'Dear Parker,' he stretched a spindly arm down from a vast, shadowy height to pat my dog, 'I did notice one thing. The squirrel in the garden has been badly glued. Clearly it has suffered a fall.'

'I hadn't noticed that,' I said. 'It must have been the gardener.'

Too late I remembered that there *was* no gardener, except me, but Max wasn't that interested: something else had enthused him. He waved a box in front of me.

'Look,' he said. 'Look! I found it at the Pasadena flea-market. This is the real America. It's the *OJ Simpson Trial Trivia Quiz.*'

Late that night, Parker and I set off to Ireland.

6

'Do you mind if I bring the dog in?' I asked the hairdresser. She paused in mid-snip, and smiled as she saw Parker in the mirror.

By the fourth day of our Irish trip, Parker and I had reached Castletownbere, a bustling, fishy port on the Beara Peninsula in West Cork. My hair was long and filthy and I was desperate for a cut. After bars, hairdressers seem to be the most frequent shops in Irish towns but whenever I had tried one, it had been 'closed for lunch' or 'back in five minutes'. At long last, the long lunch was over.

'Sure, no,' said the girl. 'He's a nice little doggie. Will he be a Kerry Blue?'

We chatted about this and that as she snipped away and I was just describing the early morning we had spent scrambling around the cliffs, how green the rocks and blue the early light had been, and how the sea had flashed like sparks struck from flint, and how – ho ho – my dog had developed a taste for sea-weed, when there was an awful cough from under the hairdryers and Parker threw up half the vegetable residue of the Atlantic.

'Oh, not to worry. It doesn't smell so bad as human puke,' said the girl, as if piles of human puke were part of the job of hairdressing in a small town. How easygoing the Irish are, I thought. When I saw my reflection I realised she had revenged herself by giving me a haircut a hungry rat could have bested. For all the unfailing charm, what an Irishman or -woman *really* thinks lies a long way back behind their eyes.

There was no real plan to the Irish jaunt. The general idea was to stick to the coast, and follow our noses. I had decided that the trip would be part of re-education in life. I would learn to enjoy silly things. I would take a lead from Parker, and go for a sniff without any preconceived ideas of happiness. The dog didn't know what to expect, but he was an optimist, and I would go along with that. Instead of trying to do what I thought I *ought* to do, instead of being sensible and ending up feeling foolish, I should start off foolish. And I would exclude from the trip any high culture or history. It would be a sensory experience.

Many of my holidays had been ruined by history. When I was a child we'd lived in Italy, and I'd gone on archaeological digs around Naples where half the buildings seemed to be Roman, and all sinking neglected into pools of stagnant water. I liked old buildings and had my own little collection of glass and pottery, but this childish fun grew into an adult difficulty. Ever since, I'd approached holidays or travelling with an educational agenda that protected me from human contact. I always had a guide to hand and made a point of stopping to look at worthy ruins. As a consequence I had a boxful of guides to cathedrals and churches, museums and galleries, but my enduring memory was of walking around large cold places with a feeling of uneasy reverence. This time, I just took some large-scale maps.

The only thing I knew for sure was that I wanted to be next to the Atlantic and swim a lot. Watching the swell, I was awestruck by the thought that there was nothing between me and New York but this fierce green and black saltwater. It was mid-August, towards the end of summer; the sun stayed close to the horizon and at sunset, the edge of the land caught the water's phosphorescence and seemed to burn dully.

When I went swimming I was occasionally alarmed by the undertow that took me away from the beach. There, on the sand, Parker would sit head on one side, ears cocked in bewilderment. Why on earth would I want to go in that huge, cold bath?

The trip had begun inauspiciously, with the cancellation of our early-morning sailing from Fishguard. Hard-driven rain scored a grey sky and it looked as though the gloomy prophets who had forecast a wash-out for me would be proved right. Somewhere in the middle of the Irish Sea our luck changed, for we rolled off the ramp at Rosslare into brilliant sunshine. We camped south of the port, near St Margaret's Beach. The sunset was peachy, there were crabs for the dog and a stack of Irish hounds splashing through the surf. Parker discovered good things about beaches: sand was easy to dig and the level horizon let him see other dogs a mile off, and streak towards them.

There were some ruins of stately homes, twined with ivy and overgrown with nettles and briars, but they seemed so much part of the landscape I never felt the urge to ask myself who had lived there and when their world had fallen apart.

The morning brought even better weather, with a horse wading through the sea and the first abandoned sandcastles to mark. Throughout the trip Parker inscribed his signature on sea-wrack and sheer cliffs, at the tops of mountains and on the banks of remote streams. 'Parker was here,' he graffitied in places that would never see another dog.

We trundled westwards towards the Beara, with Parker bouncing up and down in the back. In all, he was to spend 1500 miles and a couple of nights in the Landrover, stretched out on the sleeping bags and tents. Sometimes he put his head on my shoulder to see what was going on. He took a keen interest in passengers. I gave a few lifts: to hikers, to a window cleaner from Clonakilty, to a sponger from Cork, who said he'd pray for me if I gave him a pound, and to a vegetable-picker from Wexford who longed for an 'attack-dog, like a Dalmatian'.

'An Alsatian?'

'No,' he said, determined. 'A Dalmatian.'

West of Killarney I picked up a tramp with a face like a split tomato on his way to the Puck Fair in Killorgin 'to see the goat they put on the stand'. He stank like a barrel of old fish-heads and even Parker retreated. 'You're an awful fast driver,' he said, clamping his huge red hands on the sides of the seat and peering at the speedometer, which was reading 35 mph.

His face seemed familiar. 'It's a fine city, London,' he said. 'Was you ever in Camden Town or Islington?' It was the only time I felt I hadn't travelled very far.

En route, Parker and I camped in Wexford, on Goat Island, a rocky promontory above a little beach we were directed to by a laconic local who came up to me to talk about dogs.

The man had once been a builder in London but had joined the influx to the revitalised Ireland. He had few complaints about life, but one of his grumbles – which I heard echoed by others over the next few days – was about the Romanians coming ashore at Rosslare. Along with travellers from England, they were being blamed for an outbreak of petty crime. Many beachside car parks had new overhead barriers to prevent travellers' caravans entering them. Economic refugees were a novel experience for the Irish.

'Do you like fishing?' he asked at one point. 'If you just throw a hook into the sea from here you'll find some mackerel.'

Taken by this idea, I bought a cheap fishing rod. I hadn't fished since I was a child and though I tried and tried, I never could cast the line far enough to clear the inshore weed. At least I provided a laugh for the Irish children, hauling in their catches alongside me.

Parker proved a disappointing sentinel. On Goat Island, I pitched the tent and we spent the night on the cliffs, alone with the moon and the sighing sea. In the early hours I woke up to hear a car-door slamming. My dog was flat-out, squeaking in his sleep, dreaming of crabs and slippery rocks. Two sets of feet giggled and staggered past the tent and made their way down to the beach. After a while, they returned.

'Come on, then, Betty,' said a man. 'Get in.'

'That was great. You'll be on Viagra, then.'

With a splatter of laughter, they drove off. The pharmaceutical production of Viagra, I read in an Irish newspaper, is one of the sources of Catholic Ireland's new wealth.

After my haircut, we continued west from Castletownbere along the Beara Peninsula. I had been told that I should go to Kerry and Dingle, but locals warned me that the traffic would be terrible, that Dingle folk weren't so friendly and would try and flog me a tube of dirt for £7. The weather turned sour. For a while the road left the coast and wound inland through dripping stony mountains. It was cold and lonely. My heart sank and I asked myself what I was doing here. I hadn't had a shower or shaved for days and I had a vision of myself, aged thirty-four, dressed in dirty old pants and a tattered sweater, alone with a terrier at the edge of the Western World, going about a holiday with the inappropriate courage of Tony Hancock giving blood. Shouldn't I just go back to London and put on some sensible clothes? I could just turn north, go over the mountains to Kerry. There'd be lots of smart campsites there, perhaps even hotels where they'd let the dog in. There was no epiphany: I couldn't stop and turn around, because there was no hard shoulder, so we just thundered on and eventually the road broke out along the coast again and we came down into Allihies.

There was really nothing to the village but a row of brightly painted houses and bars ascending the slopes of the Slieve Miskish Mountains. Below it was Ballydonegan Strand, a sickle of white beach adjoined by a rough campsite dotted with domed tents that looked like the shelters of a tribe that had just crawled from the water.

I fell in love with the place and we stayed for four days. The sun came out and I took Parker scrambling up cliffs and walked some of the Ring of Beara. He would go anywhere except into the sea, but stood guard over my clothes while I swam. If I was too long on the beach, he just wandered back to the tent. We made new friends and one scalding afternoon, we went with them to Dursey Island, a massive grassy boulder at the end of the peninsula, once home to a thriving farming community, now deserted but for six people. It can only be reached by a battered cable car that sways a couple of hundred feet above the Atlantic.

Maximum load 6 persons read a notice.

'To be honest,' said a builder restoring a derelict cottage on the island, 'we've had seventeen in here.'

'Where are the emergency instructions?' muttered a lad from Leicester. Above his head he came across a prayer sellotaped to the woodwork.

The campsite was filled with dogs. There was a brown terrier mongrel who belonged to Eileen in the post-office, but had attached himself to an exasperated Irish family in a caravan and every day marked their drying towels, and two little Yorkies, origin unknown, who walked the lanes and fields day and night growling like puffing trains. Parker first fought then fell in with this crowd and together they would inspect and police the dogs who appeared for a day or a night. I set a strict curfew for Parker but in the early hours he would sneak out of the tent for more fun. When I got up, I whistled and he would come running from the beach, or from some distant stand-off.

At night Allihies was packed with locals and young Dubliners, moving from the Lighthouse Bar to O'Sullivan's and back. It was dangerously friendly. 'There was a Cohu up here before,' a mountainous farmer told me. 'Sure. Up at Coom. A Cohu. No more. Gone now.'

Maybe there was, or maybe the farmer would have said the same whatever my surname. One evening I was staggering home down the road when Parker shot off into a bar and was lost to sight. I spent twenty minutes looking for him under the feet of fiddle players, cursing myself for being so drunk and for having a black dog on a black night, only to find him sitting on the other side of the road, pleased as punch. He'd gone in the front door and straight out the back.

Once or twice I did forget myself and lapse back into

a ponderous other person. I was trying to charm a girl from Dublin when some dull voice from inside of me said, 'So what do you do for a living?'

'Oh God. Not now,' she sighed. 'I'm on me hols.'

It was a salutary lesson. Parker supplied me with introductions to several women. I was smarting from recent experiences, but at some point I had a blinding realisation that there were all sorts of ways potential romance could play out. I didn't have to be greedy: I didn't have to have an affair because it was on offer, or long for one because it wasn't. It didn't have to end badly because it didn't even have to begin. I could just be friends, have a laugh, and leave it at that.

Despite my best efforts at ignorance, it was impossible not to absorb some of the history of Allihies, partly because the Irish gossip about their history as if it had happened just the other day.

For nearly 200 years the area had been a centre for copper mining, and the remains of the mines – tunnels and chimneys – dotted and pocked the lower slopes of the mountains. It looked a bit like the Penwith Peninsula in Cornwall. There was in fact a Cornish connection, as the mine owners of the nineteenth century had imported Cornishmen to supervise their operations at Allihies. One Cornish family remains in Allihies to this day.

The beautiful white sands of Ballydonegan were, it turned out, not a natural beach at all but the residue of mining operations. The locals liked to say that the sand had come 'through the thighs of women' because women used to stand in the streams at the mines and sort the copper from the quartz. Ballydonegan is a notoriously treacherous bay: its mouth lies open to the Atlantic gales and the sea-bed is littered with wrecks of coal and ore ships. When I was there, the only concession to the dangers was a sign saying *Bathing Unsafe* lying on its side, half-covered by the sand.

Along the coast is Dunboy Castle, home of the Puxley family, originally from Swansea, who became rich through the mines. The castle was burned down by the IRA in the 1920s. By then the mines were failing and the family had pretty much retreated to Wales. The castle remains a majestic wreck. A man living in a cottage by the gate, surrounded by cages of pheasants and dogs, took a couple of quid off me and let me in. I asked him who owned the castle, and he told me his uncle did. He'd bought it off the government a long time ago. Now his cows splash about inside the Gothic hallway. 'Do you think it'll ever be rebuilt?' I asked him.

'No,' he said. 'But, then, it makes a very pretty ruin.'

Eventually, the sky turned grey again. I dragged Parker off the beach and drove north to Kerry, much against local advice as Kerry people generally weren't considered as friendly as Beara folk. By now I had realised that no part of Ireland was as friendly as the part in which one currently stood. All the same, I suspected that the Beara would remain both mine and my dog's favourite memory.

One cold wet night, we camped in the Kerry Mountains, where Parker was seriously spooked by the Little People and ran away, then we headed back to the sea. Near Tralee I gave a lift to a mother and son returning from the dentist to their home at Castlegregory on the north Dingle coast. 'It's a lovely friendly place,' she said. 'The West Kerry folk aren't so friendly. If it's sea you're after, you won't get better than Castlegregory.'

We passed three houses before I dropped her off

at a quiet crossroads. 'Which way is it into town?'
I asked.

'Well,' she said patiently, 'that was it.'

We took a pitch at The Warrens, a campsite with
a respectable façade and loos sunk in the kind of
ammonia-scented darkness eulogised by Joe Orton. The
first bar we tried that evening was decorated with empty
cornflakes packets: in the corner a small man with a
large beard was singing, 'Ooh baby, baby, it's a wild
world.'

Things didn't look too good. Where on earth was the
party? Once again, Parker turned up trumps. Outside
Fitzgerald's pub, Parker met Jake, a tall, black and
white mongrel who looked a bit like a small Afghan.
His owner was Jo, an artist from Dorset. She was staying in a van among the dunes with her friend Lorna
who had given over her job teaching hairdressing in
Dublin and was having a holiday before returning to
England.

The girls looked like a pair of pixies and had been
making money at fairs by drawing and braiding hair. On
the way down they had spent a few days at a travellers'
commune.

'Because we had a cool-box, the kids ran after us
throwing stones and shouting "weirdos, weirdos",' said
Lorna.

At their invitation, Parker and I set up home opposite
their van on the Bay of Tralee. Jo and Lorna were No.
1 Sandy Lane, we were No. 2. Jake took one side of
the track, Parker the other. When strangers came they
joined forces but otherwise kept a neighbourly distance.
Parker actively discouraged Jake from accompanying us
on our walks.

It was a breezy coastline, popular with windsurfers.

Strange creatures occasionally lurched out of the sea-mist. One morning I woke to sounds of howling. Looking out I saw Parker set on by three other dogs. When I shouted, they vanished over the dunes. We never saw them again.

The wind blew hard on the tent and I had a touch of the 'nylon nightmares'. After four days we said goodbye to our neighbours and made our way slowly back to Rosslare via Carrick on Suir, Tipperary. In town, we were followed by a chain of Tipperary strays who showed a heartbreaking patience and obstinacy in their quest for a dog-owner.

Our campsite boasted four boxers, four Dalmatians and a pack of schnauzers. When an Englishwoman asked me if I was 'showing my dog' I cottoned on. There were four dog-shows around Tipperary.

With the car packed up again I was listening to the soothing litany of auction prices on Tip Radio – 'one heifer, 340 kilos, 427 pounds. Two heifers, 280 kilos, 480 pounds . . .' when news came on that a bomb had gone off in Omagh, murdering women, children and babies.

It was an act of perplexing megalomania that I couldn't square with the time I'd had and people I'd met, with the Ireland of Viagra and housing shortages, tourism and tolerance, an Ireland that now treated its history with circumspection. I felt an utter fool. I'd been wandering around like Fotherington Thomas, saying, 'Hello birds, hello sky,' only seeing what I wanted to see. Here was the history I'd turned my back on. I thought of the crucifix-surmounted Republican memorials in every Irish village and wondered what the leaders of 1916 would make of this.

The news had got around the campsite. 'Animals!' someone shouted. 'Animals!'

No, they're humans, I thought. This was the real world. This was life. Then again, why should it be? It was a maniac's version of the world, made in the dark, out of old dead things.

The moment we returned to London I was ready to go off again. St Jude's was empty: Adèle had her roof back, Percy was in France, Jeremy had disappeared and Max had gone back to America. I missed them. The house was huge and old while outside London seemed hot and drab, stuffed to the rafters with tourists.

A few days later Parker was attacked and bitten in Myatts Fields, Camberwell. I had had a feeling something like this was going to happen. After the holiday he was full of beans and the casual campsite brawling had sharpened his territorial instincts. He insisted on checking out every dog he came across with ferocious growls and preposterous strutting.

It happened on a wet, dark evening after we'd been to a party at a house nearby. Myatts Fields had signs prohibiting dogs but when I looked I saw plenty in there, so I thought I'd walk him round quickly. It's a polite park with a wild edge to it, with rose beds and a big open field bordered by strange trees with seeds that look like kiwi fruit.

I didn't like the look of the other dog or its owner. It was a bull terrier, waddling along like a crocodile behind a stooped, crusty man in a baseball cap. They disappeared into the shadows the other side of the field and I thought Parker had missed them. He couldn't see, but unfortunately, he could smell. By the time I called him back, my voice was lost under the sounds of snarling.

The other dog had Parker by the neck. Parker had

submitted and was squealing in fear; but the bull terrier had locked its jaws on. Its owner flapped his hands helplessly as if he was trying to conjure his dog away and left it to me to pull the animal off. It was black and white and had a thick, metal studded collar. Parker limped away, his front right paw dangling. He sat, shocked, his tongue hanging out.

Torn between rage and distress, I turned on the other man. Under the peak of his black cap he had a fuzz on his chops, cheekbones like razors and burned-out eyes.

'I didn't see yer dog,' he said. 'All Staffs are like that.'

'No, they're not,' I said. 'He's never had a problem with a Staff before. It's your dog. It's *you*.'

'All Staffs are like that,' he murmured again. Then, as if as a consolation, he said, almost pleased, 'Yeah. You know, my dog's like that with all dogs.'

His bull terrier licked its lips and blinked its crocodile eyes. It was old with grey on its muzzle, stocky and fat-headed. I checked Parker for wounds. His right leg seemed hurt but I couldn't discover any injury. When I looked up, the other dog-owner had melted into the dark.

At home I found blood on my hands and discovered a rip in Parker's shoulder. The vet said it would heal up all right, but for a day or two, Parker stuck his nose out of doors cautiously and hobbled along the pavement. It was a lesson he had to learn, that not all dogs were friendly and that he was not as big as he had thought. But when I remembered the other man's proud assertion that his dog was, well, just like that, I hated him.

Parker made a full recovery, though the incident left its mark. On our first trip out after the mauling, a Weimaraner followed us into the Ladbroke Arms.

Parker took pre-emptive action and gnashed his teeth. The other dog leapt onto its owner's lap and sat there quivering. Satisfied that he would now be left alone, Parker slumped back against the bar, beetle-browed, sore and grumpy. He dislikes pubs at the best of times: people drop lager and fag-ash on his head.

Subsequently he seemed to be sucking up to big dogs, as if he was hoping to find a protector. The first was Duke, an old Doberman he met in Ladbroke Grove, in a slippery side-street lined with rusted bent railings. I've always been wary of Doberman pinschers because they tend to be one-man dogs and they have the edgy temperament you'd expect from a bloodline that includes Rottweiler, greyhound and terrier. But there was something grand about Duke. When he saw Parker he began moaning and shaking his head, as if he was anxious to tell him something, while Parker hopped up and down, squeaking the way he did when he heard a dog barking indoors trying to get out.

'He used to have ever such a lot of fights,' said Duke's owner. 'He wouldn't start them, and to be honest, he didn't win them all. He's thirteen now.'

Duke had a grey muzzle and dull, myopic eyes and his body was scarred and bent. It sounded as if he was telling Parker about past battles and Parker was telling him about his recent trauma and asking him if he had any tips for dealing with bull terriers, or maybe offering him a bone if he'd avenge the injury.

A few days later Parker met Ella, a German shepherd who came to the Portobello antiques market on a Saturday. Ella was shy, but still reassuringly big, and Parker happily plonked himself down next to her and for a while she was his new best friend. I toyed with the idea of buying another dog, perhaps a German shepherd, but it was inconceivable that Max would tolerate my having two dogs in his house, particularly if one was a large puppy that would pee on his piano.

I mentioned the injury in the column and Parker received a bag of concerned letters. Someone even sent him a fiver that I passed on to an appropriate cause. I wrote and thanked the sender. She replied, saying that she wished I hadn't thanked her, as her husband had intercepted the mail and had scolded her for sending a dog money. This time she enclosed a tin of sardines.

Throughout the remains of summer the solitary life at St Jude's began to pall. With no sign of her master returning, Maria the cleaner was reduced to ironing my underwear. I slipped into the role of janitor, rattling around the house, stoop-shouldered, with a large bunch of keys organising the continuous repairs to the central heating and hot-water system.

This was installed by a marine engineer who remained the only man who understood how it worked, and even he was vague about the details of its operation. Pipes wailed and pumps blew up and Mike the contractor had the plumbers on duty round the clock. I saw a lot of Mike. He came from a long line of bare-chested rural hunters and when he wasn't mending St Jude's, he was generally killing things and would turn up in blood-smeared jeans that sent Parker crazy.

For a couple of weeks there was a man repainting the exterior woodwork of the house. He wore white overalls, a white hat and his boots were splattered white. In the middle of this snowstorm his face glowed hot and pink in the sun. He never spoke much, but when Parker pottered past he would always smile, come down his ladder and stroke the dog. After a few days, I noticed that Parker was beginning to turn into a Westie. His ears were white with paint. I didn't want to stop the painter being friendly, and fortunately he finished painting the house before he finished painting the dog. Most of the paint came off Parker's ears but a blob lingered, complementing his occasional grey hairs, which as I told people who remarked on them, came from the strain of living with me.

My sister Lucy had a flat down the road in Shepherds Bush, where Parker had stayed a few times when I'd had to go away. He got on well with her cats. One day she called and said that she was moving with her boyfriend Thanassi to a flat on the Portobello Road, above an antiques arcade owned by Thanassi's father. There was a small flat underneath theirs that I could rent. Would I be interested? I had been wondering where I should live next and had even thought about taking a winter let in Dorset, but when I looked at the little flat on the Portobello, I knew straight away that it would suit us. It was small and scruffy, having served as a crash-pad for any number of Portobello lads, but it had lots of light and the predominantly red colour-scheme could be covered with a lick of paint.

I said I'd take it in the autumn, when Max came back. My sense of obligation towards my absentee landlord prevented me from abandoning St Jude's altogether. After all, St Jude was the patron saint of hopeless causes and he'd not yet given up on me.

Partly because I was nervous about leaving St Jude's empty, we stayed in Notting Hill for the Carnival weekend. On the Saturday, a woman on Ladbroke Square objected violently when she saw Parker cock his leg on her front steps. I took her point, and apologised, but her complaint seemed insignificant in the light of subsequent events. For the next forty-eight hours of the Carnival, every doorway and basement staircase served as a urinal or worse. No one complained. The tolerance that the wealthier inhabitants show for this must be their tithe to the general population.

St Jude's had a conveniently recessed front entrance. By Sunday night this was awash with piss and those using the facilities showed their appreciation by pressing the entry-buzzer afterwards, presumably because they thought it would flush the doorway.

On the Sunday evening, I was walking Parker in Ladbroke Square when we saw unacceptable non-urinary activity in a basement area – a man fiddling with a window latch while a companion stood nearby, keeping a look-out. I fetched the police who subsequently told me that the man claimed he was just relieving himself, but the glass was broken and they reckoned it had been an intended burglary. They were just a bit late to catch him red-handed.

I felt sheepish. Like my dog, I've always imagined myself more courageous than I am and I felt I ought not to have waited for the police. I resolved to show a bit more fight. The next night, I was walking Parker and saw a man keeping watch at the top of a flight of basement steps while someone was busy at the bottom. Here we go again, I thought, and determined this time to act promptly. The words did not come out as intended.

'Excuse me,' I said to a looming crop-headed man, 'but are you by any chance burgling that flat?'

'Nah mate,' he said. 'I'm just standing here while my bird has a slash.'

'Oh, that's all right then,' I said and made some joke about being as relieved as she was. Of course, peeing on someone's doorstep isn't in itself acceptable but under those circumstances, rights and wrongs become relative. After all, I wondered, where do the 6000 policemen go to have a pee during the Carnival?

7

One autumn day we walked past a small café off Notting Hill Gate and there, sitting in the open window, was a fox. At least, it looked like a fox. It was a small, lithe dog with a rusty-coloured coat and a curly brush. It was watching everyone that went past with curious, quick, dark eyes and when it saw Parker it pricked up its ears in interest, hopped out of the window and began to attack his whiskers.

The dog, it turned out was called Foxy and she had a wildness that went deeper than looks. She belonged to Lisa who ran the café called Food on the Hill. On each table was a photograph of Foxy above a printed request to ignore her pleas: *Hi! My name is Foxy, you may see me about the place. I'm really very sweet, but you mustn't feed me.*

Foxy was a former Battersea dog, a happy-go-lucky stray who knew fifty ways to beg and ingratiate, all done with streetwise nonchalance. When Lisa was angry with her, she rolled over on her back and showed her belly. 'Damaged, manipulative child,' Lisa sighed. Her forgiveness secured, Foxy hopped up and trotted back to doing whatever it was that had got her into trouble in the first place.

Many dogs took a shine to Parker's whiskers, particularly girlie dogs, and Foxy ragged him mercilessly, circling him and darting in to nip at his beard. He eventually took to hiding head-first in small corners – at which Foxy nipped his bum.

In Kensington Gardens, Foxy was a blur of red hair and spiky hackles, covering half the park in the time it took Parker to plod from the gates to the first tree. She leaped at passing pigeons and baited the swans in the lake, curling her lips at them when they hissed. From her days on the street she knew that where there was water, she'd find people feeding the ducks, and that these bird-people always had a spare scrap of stale bread that they'd give to a starving dog.

While Parker was nose-deep in sniffs, she launched sneak attacks that sent him tumbling. He learned to keep a eye out for her, peering around from under his beetle-brows when he cocked his leg. He developed a canny body-swerve, hopping to the left to draw her, then shimmying to the right and breaking for open country. He was soon selling Foxy this dummy in an absent-minded way.

Despite the suffering of his poor whiskers Parker liked Foxy and always wanted to visit Food on the Hill. I discovered that there were reasons other than Foxy's company. Upstairs, Foxy had a cosy basket and in it was generally a huge bone from the kitchen. Parker couldn't really have bones at St Jude's as Maria the cleaner would have had a fit, so he gnashed with joy on Foxy's bone. She didn't seem to mind. Perhaps it was her natural generosity, or perhaps as a former stray she didn't have any concept of possession. Whether it was through her kindness or insecurity, Parker found her to be one of the most virtuous dogs he had met.

Foxy was one of a number of former Battersea dogs we knew. It was a while before I went to Battersea myself, and when I did, I had quite a shock. The Dogs' Home was forever on television at that time, and it looked nice enough through the camera. Television didn't capture the pathos of the place. Leaving its clean, calm corridors, I stepped into the kennels and was drowned in the smell and noise of dogs, hundreds of barking, excited, sad, hopeful, frightened, needy dogs.

Lost dogs end up at Battersea. Not just strays, but dogs whose purpose in life has gone: their owners have died, or can't look after them any more, they have been used as guard dogs then discarded, or have been bought as puppies but just grew up. Many of the dogs I saw were German shepherds or bull terriers, or crosses between these breeds of guard dogs, the miscegenate and maltreated offspring of urban fear.

Battersea is probably the most famous charity in Britain. It attracts large donations – legend has it that on one occasion someone left a package on the doorstep containing £50,000. Public generosity is matched by public expectations. All the publicity television gener-ated led to the Home being inundated with unwanted dogs. It looked so friendly, the staff so kind that many shifty owners thought they'd be doing their pets a favour by offloading them. I felt rather ambivalent when I heard that the Home was going to expand its capacity. I wish the place wasn't necessary.

Another animal charity, the Blue Cross, invited us to its annual Dogs at Work Awards, which was held at a City conference hall, one of those banqueting suites where pension funds hold the annual back-slapping ceremony. From the moment we arrived, I thought I was losing my mind. On a raised podium, a suit was reading a short list of contenders for a workplace prize, praising the efforts of a chap called Oscar. He detailed Oscar's record at a firm of chartered accountants, his winning way with customers – what a firm handshake he had! – and the charity work Oscar did in his spare time, visiting nursing homes and hospitals. Oscar was conscientious, hardworking and kind. Oscar was the perfect employee. Oscar was a bearded collie crossed with a Tibetan terrier.

The audience barked with a mixture of enthusiasm, envy, anger, hunger and lust. The audience was, in fact, a pack of dogs. They were everywhere: under tables, on laps, noses on napkins, leads wrapped around chair-legs. It was their big day out and they didn't understand a word of it.

Parker could not believe his luck. I'd dragged him through the City along some of the most smell-sterile streets known to a dog, and at the end of it was a canine conference. He behaved dreadfully: unkempt and unwashed, he tipped chairs over as he chased after spruce bottoms, and had a prolonged stand-off with a bull terrier who stalked him Chindit-style through a jungle of chair legs and trailing tablecloths.

For several years the Blue Cross had been promoting the integration of pets into the workplace as a way to encourage people to adopt rescued dogs. There were awards for working mutts from all areas. Clerical Canines, Media Mutts, Bonio Do Gooders, Teacher's Pet and Artistic Canines. Arguably, there are great benefits to dog-ownership: owners apparently visit the doctor less, make quicker recoveries from heart attacks, get on better with their spouses and have lower blood pressure. In the workplace, it appears, dogs help to relieve stress.

They can also create it, of course. The morning concluded in canine chaos when John McCririck, the betting pundit, took the winners for a photocall. Man and dogs became hopelessly tangled, and McCririck, looking like Mr Pickwick dressed as one of the earlier Doctor Whos, was whirled round and round in a tornado of leads and tails.

It was all great fun but I couldn't help thinking that as far as the unconverted were concerned, the day had a peculiar madness that would be understood only by dog-owners, and only by a certain kind of owner at that. I put myself in a dog-hater's shoes, imagined an office full of dogs and dog-owners, and was suddenly overwhelmed by imaginary conversations about diet and bowel habits and where-they-sleep. As for Oscar, the perfect employee – and a fine overall winner – who wanted to suffer by comparison with a dog? Imagine being told by your boss that you're in a bad mood and must go and stroke the office dogsbody. It could become a tyranny of cuteness, and just the sort of thing to put people who had been thinking about taking on a dog right off the idea. I liked having a dog at work, but then I had my own dog and my own office.

We met another notable rescue dog that month, when the *Daily Telegraph* suggested that Parker might like to interview Buster, pet dog of Roy Hattersley, novelist and former deputy leader of the Labour Party. Buster had just published a diary, which Roy had obligingly ghosted for him.

I knew a bit about Buster, because the dog became a celebrity villain a few years ago when it fatally wounded a goose in St James's Park. Poor Hattersley went through hell afterwards with the press, who portrayed the dog as a malevolent stray for whom Roy had formed an unaccountable sentimental attachment.

Buster had a chequered past: he had no idea who

his father was, had been a stray, and was on Death Row when Roy took up his cause. The diary was a first-hand account of the dog's struggle to overcome his puppyhood trauma and lupine instincts and settle down to a comfortable life in London SW1. Much was made of Buster's lively nature but in the way of these things, I thought I would find that there was a fair amount of exaggeration involved. After all, Hattersley is a slighter figure than either the caricatures of him or his prose style would suggest. I expected that Buster, half-Alsatian and half-bull terrier though he is, would be a bit of a pooch.

We met on a bright but chilly autumn morning. Roy, who was due to talk on Ned Sherrin's Radio 4 programme *Loose Ends,* was dressed for a radio appearance in white cords, Burgundy sweater, tight blue shirt, silk tie and herring-bone jacket. Hurrying through Green Park, he carried in one hand a plastic bag of dog excrement, the product of Buster, a muscular animal in skin-tight green and brown camouflage who pulled strongly at his lead. The effect was of a Womble taking Cerberus for a walk.

Parker trailed behind. His one attempted sniff at Buster had been greeted with open jaws, and he thereafter played gooseberry. I had a tape recorder with me, and faithfully transcribed the encounter, quoting both man and dog, who seemed to understand each other so well that they were at times, one and the same.

Roy: [With relief as he sights a bin] Thank heavens for that. Ever since I've had a dog I've been furious with anyone I see not picking up their excrement. They give me a bad name . . .

Buster: [showing a set of perfect fangs] Hrrh! Hrrh!

Roy: Sit, Buster. Good boy.
[Roy pats him proudly. I see something being transferred surreptitiously into the dog's mouth: a biscuit, which seems to have popped out of Roy's sleeve, like an ace produced by a card-sharp.]

Roy: [shooting me a shifty look] Heh, heh. You didn't see that. You're supposed to think it's all love.

Buster: Hrrh! Ruff!

Roy: I have to warn you, he may jump. He doesn't mean any harm.

Buster: Aowh!

Me: In the book . . . [Buster leaps at the tape recorder]

Roy: Buster! It's not an offensive weapon!

Me: . . . I was struck by the number of restraining devices employed. 'Buster's braces' to hold him in the car, the 'halti' which you describe as a 'politically correct' anti-biting harness. And then there's the Baskerville . . .

Roy: Heh heh. The Baskerville . . . wretched thing. It's a kind of large muzzle. He barely knows he's got it on. I got it after an . . . incident . . . on the

train – it's in the book. After that I thought it
was better if he wore it on railway trains. In case
he should wake up and get . . . apprehensive.

Buster: Grrrrr. Grrrrr.

There were several 'incidents' in the diaries, I recalled,
besides the goose in St James's Park. A girl dancing
down the street had her sleeve torn; a reputedly ferocious feral cat in an hotel was severely ragged; a train
conductor made a sudden movement and was left with
one trouser-leg to stand in. I had presumed before
meeting Buster that these might be fictitious events:
having seen him in the flesh, I wondered what other
'incidents' Roy had omitted. As Buster led us towards
the heart of the park, Roy, bright-eyed, laughing and
happily indiscreet about his dog, was nonetheless keeping a sharp look-out for other animals. When he saw
another dog he paused and looked anxiously.

Me: How did you come to get the dog?

Roy: I was brought up with dogs. When I became a
Member of Parliament I still had my childhood
dog. She went to my mother. I thought it would
be unfair to have a dog in London. After thirty
years of deprivation when I knew I wasn't standing again, I decided to have a dog . . .

Buster: [staring at Roy] Wuff . . .

Roy: Shut up. Sit down. [Roy looks at me apologetically.] He doesn't want me to talk to you.

Buster: Grrr. Wuff.

At this point, another biscuit shot down the sleeve. Buster reminded me of a battering ram. He had so much energy that his mixed instincts seemed barely contained within his hide. About two foot high, he looked much taller, possibly because of his upright leathery ears and his tail, as stiff as a scorpion's sting. He wasn't the dog I would have associated with Roy, who Jeremy Paxman once described as 'a faithful basset hound lolloping up to his new masters with old items of Labour policy that he has retrieved from the skip of history'. The worst Roy had been accused of was congeniality, while Buster, his dog, had killed.

> *Roy:* I now think I was quite wrong not to have had a dog earlier. Better for a rescue dog to be looked after and loved in London than not at all. Now, let's see ... [He lets Buster off the lead and the dog is away, like something out of *Jurassic Park*. Parker flees.] Buster was in a Home and no one would have him because they were afraid he'd grow up into a pit-bull, which of course he won't. And he would have been the first to go in a cull ... so it was, heh, heh, an old Labour decision, the disadvantaged and the dispossessed. [Buster chews at something under a tree.] Just let me get him back on the lead. No, Buster. Heh, heh. Remember what Marcia Williams said of Harold Wilson: 'If Harold has a vice it's eating too much ketchup.' If Buster has a vice it's being greedy. He's a very greedy dog.

Me: I find that strays do tend to go back to their scrounging habits.

Roy: [a touch hurt] He's rather taken by me. [Another biscuit slips between the white teeth.]

Me: So the book . . .

Roy: Let's sit here on this bench.

Buster: Hrah! Hrah! Hrmm! Hrmm! Grrrr! Wuff! Wuff!

Roy: He never used to bark, you know. It's all the fault of the *Sunday Telegraph.* [Sitting at Roy's feet, Buster whines, grumbles and pants furiously and only fragments of Roy's complaints remain discernible through those of his dog.] Yes, a lot of silly stories . . . Buster barking at postman . . . rubbish . . . I was reading this to Buster . . . began to bark . . . never stopped since. Heh heh.

Buster: Arragh! Ruff! Ruff!

Me: So the idea for the book . . . ?

Roy: I spend a lot of time on my own and I talk to him. Heh heh.

Buster: Eeeeah! Eeeah! Huff! Huff!

Roy: . . . various stages . . . wondering what he would say . . . then in the final stage it degenerates into absolute lunacy. The idea was the inner – turmoil

– it occurred to me he must have felt, wanting to go on being wild or wanting the pleasures of not being wild. I guess he liked chasing rats around Paddington recreation ground. On the other hand he likes sleeping on a bed next to a radiator. The theme of the book is reconciling the wolf inside him with the advantages of civilisation.

Me: So it's a story of reform, a sort of *Dogmalion.*

Roy: Exactly. Yes. Heh heh.

Me: How did you feel about having him castrated?

Roy: [With a face of abject sorrow and regret.] Awful. It was fine for him, but I felt awful. It was because he was suffering so much sexual torment. He used to sit in his basket in a state of obvious excitement, howling hour after hour. My mother said, 'he wants to go courting' . . .'

Buster: Eowhh! Eowhh!!Hrrr! Hrrr!

[I suffer a moment of panic. Caught up in this tale of transformation, I have lost sight of Parker. At last I see him investigating a Golden Retriever and call him back. The other dog follows.]

Me: I had imagined Buster would talk in a Northern accent. But it's more like *Oliver Twist* or *Fanny Hill,* for that matter. When he says he finds you brushing him 'erotic' . . .

Roy: Heh! Heh! I didn't want to do one of those books where dogs have opinions on everything. Buster has no views on whether Clinton should be impeached. He has views on walks, food and biting things. I thought he might talk as if he came from Dudley, in the West Midlands. But he came out a literary dog. That's me, showing off. Heh! Heh! [In the book Buster did, in fact, prove a handy vehicle for the odd sly opinion, on Norman Tebbit, for example, whose dogs were an unhealthy model of discipline. But Roy, of course, was not responsible for his dog's opinions.]

Me: He compares his barking to Lizzie Bennet's coughs.

Roy: Yes. Heh heh. And when I appear on *Loose Ends* later and Ned asks me about the killing of the goose, Buster's answer, through me, will be like Mr Wilcox in *Howards' End* who says, 'I am a man and have a man's vices', I shall also offer the E. M. Forster defence: 'I am a dog and have a dog's vices.'

[Buster watches the retriever come closer. Roy winds him in on the lead. It all goes rather quiet. A little way off, Parker sits innocently examining a leaf caught in his tail.]

Roy: Ah. Let's see what . . . goodness . . .

Me: He's very strong.

Roy: . . . His shoulder will be dislocated sooner or later. The question is . . .

Buster: Hrrrrh! Hrrrrrh! Hrr*aaah*!
    [The two dogs leap at each other and a brief mélée ensues. After some harsh words the retriever is sent on its way and Roy, panting and a touch pale, brings his literary collaborator to heel.]

Roy: My fear is . . . I don't think Buster will start something. My fear is that he'll finish it. You see, that dog curled its lip and Buster thought, We're not having any of this. We're not risking it.

Me: Ah, yes. Probably thought he was protecting the pack.

Roy: Yes. Yes. You see, it's like that business of the feral cat in the hotel. If the owner hadn't been so proud of the ferocity of his cat . . . [He shakes his head.]

Buster: Hah! Hah! Heh! Hrrrh!

[We turn back towards the edge of the park.]

Me: Do you find yourself getting muddled up with the dog, as if he were an extension of you?

Roy: Oh yes. There's a bit in the book where Buster says: 'I'm not sure he loves me for myself but because I'm the dog he always wanted to be and never could be . . .'

Buster: Huff! Huff! [He stares up at Roy, his eyes brimming with adoration.]

Roy: [stirred and unashamed] I totally admire him. His courage, his strength. I admire his apparent optimism. I admire the way he leaps in the air to try and catch birds, even though he'll never catch one.

Me: Can you imagine your life without him?

Roy: No. I do all I can to extend his life. I dote on him. It's rather silly, I suppose. After the goose incident, when lots of crank letters said he should be shot, I thought that if there was a risk of him being put down, then madly, insanely, lunatically I'd have taken him to Ireland. [A moment of unforced pathos. Roy looks close to tears.] We'd have run away together. It would have been a marvellous end to the romance. A rather unhealthy end. Heh, heh.

Buster: Aawh. Aawh! Hrrrah!

We shook hands and the pair of them walked off towards Buckingham Palace. Autumnal tranquillity returned and Parker reappeared and slipped back alongside me. From behind various trees, other dog-owners now emerged. One of these, whose identity I feel obliged to protect, alluded darkly to an early incident involving her Westie, that almost ended in tragedy. It did not feature in the diaries, so there were indeed other 'incidents' that Buster, or Roy, had forgotten. This woman did concede that Buster had improved after he was castrated and 'sent to a psychiatrist'.

All of which strikes me as testimony to the success of Hattersley's enduring Socialist enthusiasm for improvement; by books, warm beds and biscuits, and sometimes by whatever means necessary.

8

My sister Lucy and her boyfriend Thanassi moved to the Portobello Road and I followed, taking over the flat beneath them. I still stayed part of the time at St Jude's, as I hadn't had any definite word from Max about when he intended to return. One day I received a small package from him containing a sachet of *TanTowel: the self-tanning towelette* – the instructions included the helpful warning *For External Use Only* – and a photograph of the service board outside the Los Angeles Westminster Presbyterian Church, which promised *Worship 10.30: Bungee Jumping With Jesus.* He was well, it seemed, and his usual self.

To Parker's joy, Lucy's cats Eva and Grace moved in with her. Parker knew them from the times he'd stayed with her, and he was anxious that they should feel comfortable. Slightly lost in their new environment, they wandered between the two flats and hid among the socks in my drawer. Parker watched, concerned. When they came out, cautiously picking their way through this strange world, sniffing at corners, shoes and dark cracks, he wagged his tail, wiggled his ears and then followed them around, sniffing with them. When Grace spat at him, he scuttled away, mortified. He might have fancied himself as an honorary cat, but they knew he was a dog.

Our new home had been empty for months. One

of the sash windows had dropped open and the curtains were stained with rainwater. In corners lay odd bits and pieces left by previous occupants: a toddler's plastic tricycle, an old video, a lamp in the shape of an egg that gave off a green, reptilian light. There was also a well-thumbed copy of Nancy Friday's *Women On Top*, a bunch of dried roses, an old green sofa and a soggy bed.

The sofa had seen better days and the bed, Thanassi told me with a wink, had seen everything. Despite this nugget of information I couldn't yet afford new furniture and I became fond of the sofa, as did Parker. It was squashy and full of old smells and became a favourite place for him to sleep, all paws up, growling as he dreamed. From the back he could see down into the Portobello Road and watch the dogs strutting past. Outside the window hung a large pink teapot; this unfailingly drew crowds of tourists who stood beneath it and posed for photographs. Parker often crept into the frame, peering down curiously.

The flat became a shambles of wood shavings, half-empty boxes, pots of paint and piles of paper. When Adèle stopped by, I felt I had to mention casually that I was 'doing the place up', just in case she couldn't see that for herself.

'Hrrmph. You can string that out for weeks before you have to do any washing up,' she said. Then she told me a story about Percy. After I'd gone away to Ireland he'd become fascinated with the face of a girl he'd seen on a poster in Notting Hill. *Missing: Have You Seen This Girl?* She looked foreign, dark – French perhaps. Underneath her face was a telephone number, saying *Call her Family Now*. Percy was upset at the thought of the pain this must be causing her family.

'One day he saw her,' said Adèle. A serene smile spread slowly over her face, like winter sunshine on the English Channel. 'He came in wet and excited and said he'd seen the girl. He'd had a craving for bagels and had put on a coat over his dressing gown and gone out to look for a delicatessen on Westbourne Grove, when he saw the girl coming out of Agnès B. He followed her for a bit. It was pouring with rain. Just think of him, water dripping from his nose, with that odd look in his eyes, bright and oily, and sad, like the bottom of a glass of vodka, stalking this girl wondering why, if he can see her, everybody else isn't running up and saying, "You must phone your family now." Then she waved down a cab, and was off into the rain. Percy tried to find a poster, so he could call her family, but all the posters had been pasted over. He spent hours in the rain before he found one, way up near the Golborne Road. He took the number, came home and before I could say anything to soothe him, he was on the phone.

' "That's odd," he said to me. "They say that my call will be charged at a pound a minute. I suppose it's how they're funding the search." Then he put his ear back to the receiver. "Now they're playing me music," he said. "I must be on hold." A minute later, he says, "Oh. Oh," and puts the receiver down. "What's up, Percy?" I ask him. "It was an advert," he said. "For a song called 'Have You Seen This Girl?' by a group called Family." Poor Percy. He had a terrible cold and refused to go out for the rest of his stay.'

She finished the wine I had given her and looked around for something else to drink. I imagined I saw her eyes slow fractionally as they passed a bottle of white spirit. 'Oh well. We must take the dogs out together soon,' she said. 'Rex is due for a walk in five days' time.'

Poor Percy. I could see that Adèle had wound him up, and it wasn't hard to fill in the bits of the story she'd omitted, how they'd probably just been walking down the street and she'd casually said, 'Look at that girl in the poster. My, what a pity.' It was an added bonus that he thought he'd seen her, just like Jeremy visiting a place that never existed. I sympathised with Percy. It was hard sometimes to distinguish between the performances and real lives of Notting Hill: the confusion could seem callous. The area encouraged drama. Its cosy village setting was slashed with dark streets and the shadows of cliques and cabals moved behind drawn blinds. Sometimes it seemed like a raucous adult playground. Not all of it was moneyed, and the council tenants and old immigrant community lingered to the north and west of the new restaurants on Kensington Park Road. For the wealthy new incomers, this proximity provided the illusion of a mixed community though all the different groups of the area lived very different lives and underneath there was some bitterness on the part of the old inhabitants.

It's not often in the city that you realise when you are on high ground, but Notting Hill stands just enough above its surrounding areas to give the impression of exclusivity. You seem to look down on the silky pink sunsets that lie over the west of London. Standing at the bottom of the Portobello the evening sky opened up vast and blue, as if somewhere above Oxford Gardens the world stopped and ran into the sea. Despite the bustle of the place, at certain hours it seemed deserted. As we walked up the Portobello at night, cutting through the pools of lamplight that fell across painted shutters and cobbles, the pubs would be full but we would be alone on the street. I could understand that for some people, this small world was their life's stage. For a few years, you could have fun, and then you sort of disappeared. There was a bit of slacker graffiti in Colville Square that stuck in my head. I'm sure it wasn't original, but it seemed perfect for Notting Hill.

I was here, and now I'm not
I went away to smoke some pot
I wrote this here to prove my point
That life is shit without a joint.

Walking around the streets much of the day, I was pestered by a spate of drive-by spivs flogging everything from watches to 36-inch colour television sets. For a few weeks they seemed to be everywhere, mostly driving company vans and in uniform. They'd pull up to the kerb, call me over and I'd obligingly trot across thinking they wanted directions, only to find that they were waving a delivery slip for the 'nice set of speakers' they offered to flog cheap to me. When I refused, I was inevitably called a wanker. I couldn't believe this stuff was just disappearing from shops and warehouses without anyone noticing, then came to the conclusion that these spivs must be part of a police entrapment campaign. Thanassi, who knew a great deal more about these things than I did, said that they were orthodox retailers pretending to be criminals. 'Some people like to think they're getting a bargain,' he said. 'So if you, you know, tell them that it's a bit hot, they like that. They can tell their mates they know the right people. Or the wrong people. It's hip to be dodgy.'

It was another weird West London thing.

There were dozens of films being made around Notting Hill that year. As it happened, Thanassi worked as a location manager, and Lucy one day warned me that he had agreed to let the front of the arcade be used for filming. One Friday morning I woke to find the door barricaded by girls with walkie-talkies while a stage drunk lay in the gutter.

They were shooting a scene that you could see for free most evenings, except that everyone was slightly too good-looking to be real. The cameras rolled for hours. I couldn't get out for a walk and in desperation Parker peed on a plant-pot.

On Saturday they couldn't film because of the market, but it began to bucket down and if you go out on the Portobello on a wet Saturday, you're sure to have an eye poked out by an umbrella. After an early foray so Parker could do some paperwork, I went back to decorating the flat, while the dog first made a nest out of my decent sweater then shredded a pair of socks. The bribe of a sausage was rejected and as the afternoon turned gloomy Parker vanished altogether. It was only after I had given up looking for him and slumped on the sofa that I noticed that the cushion had eyes.

On Sunday we went out for a walk first thing, but I had by now fallen under the spell of DIY and was anxious to get back to painting. I promised him a long walk, later. Later it began to rain, harder than ever. By the afternoon Parker was sulking furiously so I put him in Lucy's flat upstairs with the cats. He went and sat in their basket.

'He wants to go out all the time,' I said. 'I can't take it, just as I'm trying to make a home for us.'

'The problem is, you've spoiled him,' said my sister. 'Most dogs I know are shut up most of the day.'

She was right, but it was too late. 'He now expects things of me and I can't change that relationship,' I said. 'I'll take him out when it stops raining.'

'Is it raining down there?' she asked. 'It's not raining up here.'

I went outside to take a closer look at this meteorological phenomenon and discovered a hose-pipe on a metal stand directing a stream of water down my window. There was no other sign of the film crew, who'd come back that morning to complete a few shots and gone away, leaving only bad weather behind them. Later, a man rolled out of the pub and turned the rain off.

It was Monday before the sun came back and we could go off with Foxy to Kensington Gardens. There we met a woman with a basset hound, who knew Parker from the newspaper. Her Scottie had died a year ago and she was still missing its obdurate ways. She cut out the column every week and sent it to her sister in Zimbabwe, who had a Scottie – who sent it on to her friend in Malawi, who *used* to have a Scottie – who faxed it by satellite phone to a couple of Scottie-owners stranded in the Republic of Congo.

I realised then that I was part of a discreet but potent international Freemasonry of Scottie-owners who greeted each other with the phrase: 'We always had a Scottie when I was a child,' to which the correct response was: 'You don't see many of them nowadays.'

'Does he do any tricks?' asked the nice lady. She waved a stick at Parker and invited him to hop up and take it. Parker gave her a quizzical look and pottered off to chew a stick that was already on the ground. 'Just like my old Hamish,' she said. 'He never could see the point of tricks.'

She looked sad all the same. 'He will jump up and wave his paws, if you ask him to say hello,' I said, hoping to cheer her up.

'Say hello,' she commanded, rather than asked. Parker

gave her a wag, but his attention was fixed on a line of pekes, four or five of them, that were making their way like a procession of caterpillars across the park.

'It would be so nice if he could do the odd trick,' she said. 'I rather think my Hamish missed out. Oh look!' She pointed to a woman in jodhpurs striding along with a Labrador bounding behind her. 'She's a dog-trainer. I tried asking her for tips, but she's very coy. I suppose it's a bit like saying you're a doctor. Everyone wants advice for free.' She lowered her voice. 'All the same, one would have expected her to show a bit more camaraderie.'

Like old Hamish, I'd never seen the point of tricks either, though an essential part of controlling Foxy was food, to which end Lisa supplied me with a small bag of chocolate drops that I would wave at Foxy when she threatened to run off altogether. Foxy begged for these and I'd tried to encourage Parker to sit with her. Unfortunately, he hated chocolate, and disliked sitting as it made his bottom wet and cold.

I rationalised his behaviour: the fact that he wouldn't sit didn't make him a badly behaved dog. There were plenty of canny dogs who had worked out that if they sat when instructed their owners would overlook their many misdemeanours. It was probably the first thing old dogs told young ones: 'Listen, kid, sit when you're told to and you can do what you like the rest of the time.'

A little further on we came across the aforementioned dog-trainer conferring with a group of dog-walkers. They were handing out treats to a pack of Labs, retrievers and Jack Russells. 'Now Timmie,' the trainer would say, 'ask nicely,' and each dog in turn begged or offered a paw, or went belly up: they all had a trick. Parker slunk into the queue and stared at the dispensing hand passing to and fro.

'What a nice Scottie,' said the woman. 'Won't you ask for a biscuit?'

Parker stared at her coldly.

'Go on,' she said. 'Sit. My, won't you sit? Down. *Dowwwnnn.*'

Parker stared. She wavered.

'He's only a year old,' I put in.

'Oh, he's just a puppy. What a sweet puppy. There, Pups, have a bikkie.'

It was a lie, for he was eighteen months old, but he got the biscuit. I began to see one reason why people are obsessed with teaching their dogs to sit and so on: so that other people will feed them.

I left Parker at Food on the Hill while I went off to feed my DIY obsession with more paint. I came back to find him curled up in a tiny cardboard box that had previously contained bottles of water. It was even smaller than Lucy's cat-basket.

'He's behaving very oddly,' Lisa said. 'We were filling the fridge from the box when he just climbed in it.'

He was just trying to protect his whiskers from Foxy, but from the wistful way he looked at me, I imagined he was warning me what genuine psychological damage would follow if he was ever again denied a trip to the park for three days.

In October, Parker and I were invited to a party in Wales, to be held at the end of the month at the farm where I'd met Catherine, my ex-girlfriend. It was an important occasion as the friends who lived there were leaving for Scotland. Since I was a student I'd been a constant visitor, then Parker and I had lived half a mile away, with Pip the Scottie and Polly the cat.

'Of course I'll come,' I said, but afterwards I had second thoughts. I'd not been back to Wales for six months, apart from one occasion when I agreed to house-sit for a week. It hadn't been a happy experience. The house was said to be haunted, and I felt as if I had been assailed by ghosts who lurked in the shadowy hallway, and laughed at me very time I walked past. They were just incarnations of my own memories, but the romantically-inclined offspring of the house claimed the place had been cursed by a gypsy and was genuinely haunted by various hanged thieves. They based this assertion on the name of the hill on which the house stood – Callow, which they said was a corruption of 'gallows'. They were persuasive, and so convinced of it themselves that I believed them.

It was the actor Simon Callow who told me that Callow could mean 'brave' but in Welsh also meant 'bald'. It was not a haunted hill but a hairless hump.

Catherine was sure to be there, and we were barely on speaking terms. One of the principal disputes was ownership of a lawnmower I'd bought: whether it still belonged to me, or whether she was justified in appropriating it as a settlement in kind for various expenses she claimed. It was a fine lawnmower, a Toro, four horsepower and with a mulching facility. There was also a Strimmer, but I wasn't so attached to that. It didn't have the same domestic symbolism as a lawnmower.

The real problem was that I missed living there. I now had another life, and I didn't want to ruffle it with thoughts of what might have been. But it would be nice for Parker, I thought, if he could see Pip again, though they had probably forgotten all about each other.

It was a tricky decision to make.

When the end of the month came around, I had a ready excuse for not going to the party as I'd had four wisdom teeth removed under local anaesthetic by a brute of a dentist and didn't really feel up to it. It was like watching a violent film with the volume turned down and later, when the drugs wore off, my head treated me to the soundtrack of pain I had missed. I had the cheeks of a gorged hamster and no tablets dulled the ache.

Much to my surprise, the moment we set off I felt better, probably because the discomfort and vibration of the Landrover quite obliterated my headache. A different form of pain is often the best anaesthetic. By the time we crossed the Severn I was in a positively sunny mood.

It was a wild, end-of-term party: guests sprawled out from the house into the garden and woods and fell into the small swimming pool. At times there was so much noise it seemed the wooden walls, held together mostly by wisteria, would collapse altogether. I did see Catherine, but she was pie-eyed and neither of us said anything of any consequence. I asked her where Pip was and she said that he'd gone to bed early. 'He's become very particular about his bedtime,' she said. Clearly, she hadn't told him that Parker was here. We agreed that I should come up to our old home the next morning so the dogs could have a run around.

Parker positioned himself under the buffet, opened his eyes and mouth wide and gratefully gulped the pieces of beef guests tossed down his gullet. I got into an argument with a girl who was feeding him slice after slice. 'You're neglecting him,' she slurred at me. 'He needs love.'

Yes indeed, I do, Parker's eyes said.

I'd read somewhere that dogs don't have memories, so I was worried about the reunion between Parker and Pip. Not only would they have forgotten each other, but there would be trouble as they were both young males. In the event, their meeting was one of the high points of the year. First of all, Parker met Polly the cat, who was sunning herself on the gravel outside his old home. For several minutes they stood nose to nose, Parker talking boisterous semaphore with his tail, Polly expressing herself in more languid fashion. The news that Parker had come had by now penetrated the house, for from inside came a frantic crashing as Pip tried to get out of the cat-flap. Parker hooted and tried to get in, and became stuck, just as he used to, with his big black bottom waving outside while inside, his head conducted an ecstatic reunion with his old Scottie chum. When I extracted Parker, Pip popped out after him, like a cork from the bottle. To my delight there was nothing restrained about their meeting, and no aggression. They were thrilled to find each other again and rolled over and over like tumbleweed before setting off to chase Polly round the shrubbery.

Catherine emerged, and we had a friendly conversation about ownership of the lawnmower. She graciously offered it back to me and I graciously gave it to her. It all seemed silly now: after all, I didn't have a lawn to mow and she had never worked out how to use the wretched thing. Why did it all matter so much?

'Yip! Yip! Yip!' went the Scotties and together they rushed off to the wild woods.

After we returned to London, Parker was subdued and hid in inky corners. When the door-buzzer rang he rushed excitedly downstairs, thinking perhaps that his friend Pip had followed him up the motorway.

It must have been strange to revisit his former life for a few hours. But it was good for him, as it was for me, to know that he hadn't altogether dreamed the past, and there was once a lot of fun, as well as all the rest.

9

November came around, and Max had still not returned. When I called him he sounded lethargic and suggested that instead of him returning to England, I should visit him in Los Angeles. I booked a plane ticket and sent Parker upstairs to stay with Lucy and Thanassi.

Parker was very fond of Lucy, so much so that it was impossible not to experience a twinge of jealousy when he ran to meet her at the door. She often took him for walks and they made a striking couple. I was pleased that Parker was so easygoing, but I hoped he secretly preferred being with me. If ever I lent him out and heard that he'd had a 'lovely time' with someone else I'd always feel obliged to give him a can of tuna, just to remind him that there was no place like home. He did well out of this insecurity.

I'd discovered that there was an irritating human breed who would volunteer to look after dogs and afterwards give notes on conduct, diet and training. They were specialists in authority without responsibility, just as some people are with children. I was also worried that Parker would provide the means to attack my own character and habits: the dog was sulky, or the dog had a scab on its back and was therefore neglected. One temporary owner was concerned that Parker liked dark corners: 'Do you shout at him?' she asked. Parker had always liked dark corners, I said. When he was a puppy he liked dark corners. It sounded as if I was making an excuse.

One thing I do know is that dogs like people who take them for walks, and when I questioned the self-styled dog-experts as to where they walked the dog, I generally found it was taken no further than the corner shop. 'Oh, surely they don't need more than that?' the dog-expert would say. 'You don't want to spoil them.' Or: 'But his legs are so short!'

Lucy, of course, was not remotely like this. She genuinely enjoyed looking after Parker, and often talked about how she'd like to get a dog of her own – one small enough to carry about in the basket of her bicycle. She was an actress and when she was resting, having a dog to walk helped the days retain their structure.

We did have one on-going dispute about Parker, and that was as to whether or not he had fleas. Lucy found fleas where I could not. When I left him with her there was always the risk that I'd return to find he'd been put on some newfangled treatment for fleas involving capsules or tablets or injections. She was always very pleased by the promised efficacy of the latest treatment she'd discovered.

The flight to Los Angeles was the longest plane trip I'd ever made. I tended to think of myself as well-travelled, when in fact I was more well-thumbed. I'd never been to Asia or Australia, been to Africa only once, and in America I'd never been outside New York. In my mind I knew lots of exotic destinations intimately, and could even remember the approving – or disparaging – remarks I imagined I had made on returning from long, seedy jaunts into the belly of a foreign culture. These sardonic fantasies were the consequence of having read too many books, which taught me that all experience is ultimately disappointing. The author has already been there, and had the definitive experience. What else is there to do but follow his or her script?

The plane was full of tough old Kiwis for whom this trip was just another segment in a long bus-ride they made every two or three years to visit their far-flung families. They drank buckets of Lindauer white and swapped advice on the best pubs in London. Those were the women. I tried to sleep too, but the plane was crossing such astonishing places: Greenland, Thunder Bay, Hudson Bay, the Great Lakes, the Rocky Mountains. I couldn't see them, but the names filled my head with a jumble of images, a mixture of Victorian prints and bad television. Every few hours, we were fed a three-course meal and a film starring Kevin Costner was screened. The airline did everything to convince us that we were in a cinema, or an oddly themed restaurant, but there was no way of concealing the fact that we were having a unique, modern experience, hurtling through the atmosphere at 30,000 feet in a pressurised tube containing 350 people suffering from bad wind.

In Los Angeles, I found Max lurking in a small apartment off Wilshire Boulevard. Rather than stick me on the sofa, he had booked me into a hotel next door, the Beverly Palms. My room was up a flight of stairs at the back, overlooking balconies flowing with winter-flowering jasmine and level with the tops of spindly palms that edged the swimming pool. The room was painted sunset pink: a small humming bird, its wings a blur of brilliant blue, came and fed at my window box. On the television they promised a feast of sunshine.

To me, the Beverly Palms seemed the height of luxury

and I was confused when Max apologised for putting me in such a 'bad hotel'. 'Why's it bad?' I asked.

'It's tacky,' he said sternly. 'Would you like to go and look at some other hotel rooms?' Inspecting hotel rooms was a hobby of his.

I looked again at the Palms' façade with its marble-clad portico and revolving doors, and saw flaking gold paint and rubber plants spattered with soot from the river of cars that thundered past down Wilshire Boulevard. The swimming pool that had seemed an acre of pellucid blue, was in fact a small kidney-shape, had a crack across the bottom and tasted of pure chemicals. The carpet in the foyer was worn and greasy and my room was so secluded from daylight that the pink walls were mostly shrouded in heavy shadows that seemed to prevail as a kind of dampness when I turned on the electric lights. At the back of the room was a small dark window through which came the sound of a barking dog shut up in the apartments next door. The air-conditioning system rattled and roared and I was either frozen or suffocating. To crown it all, within twenty-four hours I had a stinking cold, which I'd not expected in a city where the temperature was in the high seventies.

'I don't know what's hit me,' I croaked to Max. His own apartment, which he shared with his girl-friend, was in a block popular with retired actresses who sat, dehydrating, in lonely pairs in a small communal garden of desert succulents and hose-pipes. Max wasn't in the best of sorts himself. He was pale and dark-eyed, though his cheekbones crackled with a radio-active tan. His body was crooked from working on the antique Amstrad word-processor he had imported at vast expense. There wasn't a desk, so he had been working over the low coffee table and, unsurprisingly, had back pains.

'Why don't you get a desk?' I asked him.

'Apathy. It's the horror of this place,' he said. 'The creeping helplessness. The *ennui.*'

To illustrate this statement, he took me to the Beverly Centre, a shopping mall equally impersonal from whatever direction it is viewed, that broods over Hollywood like a vast nuclear bunker. There are several floors of shops, but we went only as far as Pet Love, the store 'where the stars buy their pets'.

In glass-fronted cases, two walls of them, were pairs of puppies: a Rottweiler and a retriever, a spaniel and a boxer, a beagle and a Bichon Frise and dozens more. Under the white electric light the puppies looked like skinless sausages. They were well cared for, but it was the most effective presentation I ever saw. I felt so sorry for them I wanted to buy the lot.

'You can ask to see them,' said Max. 'D'you want to see one?' and he gave me a pleading look.

He asked for the boxer puppy. In a box at the bottom of one of the walls, a tiny Scottie was sleeping, oblivious to everything, as only Scotties can be. The breed is popular in America: Roosevelt had a famous Scottie and in London Parker was often stopped in the street by Americans who wanted to take his picture. I asked to see the Scottie and a girl showed us to a 'bonding cubicle'.

When she brought Max the boxer it was delighted to see him and jumped up to lick his face. 'Hello boy,' he said, cheering up. 'You stupid boxer, you.'

The puppy had been in the shop for a couple of weeks. The obvious bond between man and dog made me suspicious. 'How often have you been here?' I asked Max.

'Just once. Once or twice. Twice,' he said, looking down.

'I bet you've been here every day.'

'All right,' he whispered. 'Every day. There's nothing else to do in LA. There's no culture, no architecture, no air. I come and think of buying this lovely, stupid little boxer but I've already got a boxer in England. Then I feel incredibly disloyal and I can't.'

I wanted to tell him that he mustn't lead the boxer on, but he knew what I was thinking. 'Don't worry,' he said sadly. 'Someone else will buy it soon.'

When the Scottie was brought to the cubicle, it was very sleepy and showed no interest in me, just peed in a corner then went on a sniff patrol. Parker was from Carmarthen, Wales and this little dog from Texas, but they were definitely the same breed. The price was different: Texan Scottie was on the market for $900, five times the cost of Parker. Fortunately, Texan Scottie was available on credit.

Later, we had lunch at a beachside café in Santa Monica. A dude in shades and stubble got out of his Mercedes with a Scottie in tow. He tethered the dog to a table and went and ordered an 'iced de-caff caffe-latte with half-and-half' which I think translates as a cup of cold water with a dash of low-fat. The Scottie, name of Scout, hid under the table. Whenever a roller-blader went past, it leaped out and barked furiously. That made me feel very much at home.

I had said I wanted to go swimming, so we went on up the coast for half an hour and came to the lower reaches of Malibu, next to the old pier that housed Alice's Restaurant, now closed and derelict. There were pelicans diving from it, into the smooth, vast waters of the Pacific. Max declined to swim, and sat on the rocks and stared at the sun dropping into the west like a huge Vitamin C tablet. The undertow was subtler than the Atlantic, but more powerful, and fifty yards out, the baby-warmth of the water was infused suddenly with icy currents that hinted at the frightening enormity of the ocean.

'Los Angeles is a great place to be if you're a car,' said Max, as we drove home. 'I'm a car. Poop poop. Ha. Ha.' He was bewildered at why he felt so low. 'I had a blood test last week to see if I had anything wrong, but I was fine,' he said. 'I think I'll go for a brain scan next week. Perhaps I've got something wrong in my head.' The thought cheered him up, and he took a detour to show me the lonely reaches of Topanga Canyon, where Charles Manson's 'Family' used to live.

Something bothered me about our trip to the beach. It had been a lovely day and there were a few people on the sand, but I was the only one swimming.

'Is there a problem with sharks?' I asked Max.

'Oh no,' he said blithely. 'Nobody in their right minds would swim off Malibu. It's pretty, but the prevailing currents hold the sewage inland, you see.'

'Was that why you wouldn't swim? Why didn't you tell me?'

'Well, there are two ways of looking at this. Firstly, it may just be American paranoia. Secondly, even if it isn't, you're English and used to dirty beaches. There is even a third possibility – that what you don't know can't hurt you.'

I was sure I felt an itch coming. I looked at my arms. Was that a purple rash?

'I know a very good skin-specialist,' Max told me. 'We call him Doctor Shoot-Me-Up. He specialises in giving jabs of botoxin – you know the botulism they use to freeze wrinkles. But he's pretty good with sewage too.'

To my relief, the rash subsided within a few hours. Max already had the next horror lined up. 'Let's go to Las Vegas,' he said. 'That's truly grotesque, but the hotel rooms are surprisingly good value.' I wasn't feeling ready for Vegas, and persuaded him instead to visit Joshua Tree National Park, on the edge of the Mojave Desert, a couple of hours out of Los Angeles. It was in the direction of Vegas, he said, if I changed my mind.

We bounced eastwards over the rutted 10 Freeway. It seemed like a six-lane dirt-track, just as the city seemed like a first-world-third-world-shanty-town that sprawled in a suburban crust of bungalows and malls for a hundred miles inland. The traffic moved bumper to bumper in ferocious competition, with barely a foot to spare between lanes. There was no hard shoulder and the central reservation was a stumpy concrete lip scarred from brawls with the hurtling cars. In and out of the lanes danced pick-ups, loaded with gardening refuse, driven by Mexicans with a streak of fatalistic madness. Cut grass, scrub and empty plastic sacks flew from the pick-ups and adhered to wheels and windscreens. I was convinced we would not survive. What would Parker do without me? I could be at home now, I thought, just taking him for his evening sniffs along Denbigh Terrace.

'Not bad today, the traffic,' said Max, steering the car with one cool, dab hand. 'Not bad at all. You should see it when it rains. They had eighty-nine accidents the other morning when it rained.'

'This is terrifying.'

'I've often wondered what it would be like to be

involved in a road accident,' he said, with scholarly calm. 'There are two ways of looking at it. One the one hand, you would almost certainly be dead. On the other, you wouldn't have much time to think about it. And I don't know about you, but that's what scares me. The thinking.'

Just then, two white plastic buckets flew from the back of a passing pick-up and sailed towards our windscreen. I screamed and ducked my head. At the last second they dipped, hit the road and bounced sideways to be crushed under the double wheels of an adjacent truck. Max was unperturbed.

'Did you see that?' I shouted.

He nodded. 'Yes. But what am I supposed to do about it? I couldn't exactly stop and move them out of the way. One is on the great, mad highway of life, and *che sera sera*. By the way, I want to make this clear: it's your fault if we die. We could have flown to Las Vegas. I could have flown you personally. I have a licence, you know. We could have had fun looking at some rooms.'

We stayed that night at the Twenty-Nine Palms Inn which offered comfortable little adobe huts spread around an oasis. Roadrunners and jackrabbits scuttled through the sagebrush and the view out the back was of bare brown mountains. At night the stars were diamond sharp and crystal silence prevailed, apart from distant, wistful howling.

'Those will be coyotes,' said Max. 'I suppose they must come into town looking for prey. Make sure you lock your door.'

I could see I was being punished for refusing to go to Las Vegas.

We saw a coyote in Joshua Tree the next day. It was

wandering up the middle of the road, a spindly grey thing with big yellow eyes and a lolling tongue. It didn't look at all well. Several Americans were circling it in four-wheel drive vehicles, like Indians riding around General Custer, snapping away with cameras and videos. Otherwise the desert was empty of life. The smell was extraordinary: it smelled of absolutely nothing. Max approved. 'It's very clean,' he said. 'There's no dog shit. You know, I once had an idea for a short film along expressionist lines that would show dog-shit in the most unlikely places, and from strange angles. Up through a street grating, or on Neil Armstrong's moon-boat. After all, we may be disappointed in our quest for life on Mars, but you know damn well there's going to be dog-shit there.'

This was high desert, cool at that time of year and broken by vast formations of massive pink rocks that silent ages had smoothed to perfect spheres. They were balanced precipitously on each other like piles of rough marbles, and looked as if a cough would set them all rolling. Between the rocks were rocky valleys where our voices fell flat and small. The Joshua Trees, named after the prophet, weren't trees at all, but like the roots of trees: weird, barbed cactus growths with multiple arthritic arms, some forty-foot high. At one point we walked into a plain filled with these frozen gesticulating figures. It was a distinctly ominous sight and I thought perhaps I'd been wrong about the lack of life in the desert. There were life forms, but so still and harmonious that they were beyond my understanding.

Max was keen to press on to Las Vegas. I wasn't sure, and we argued a bit. We settled on a compromise: we would stay in the area and see how we felt, and in the meantime, Max would be allowed to 'look at some rooms'. Specifically, he wanted to look at a place called Hot Springs Ranch where they had a room called the Al Capone Suite with a bullet-hole in the window.

We found the hotel behind a barred entrance on an empty road near Desert Hot Springs. The guard, a heavy-set figure in a dusty-brown uniform, would not let us in.

'I want to take a look at some rooms,' said Max.

'You can't look at the rooms. You have to have a reservation,' he said, casting a disparaging eye over our hired Ford Mustang. Beyond the gate was a row of guests' vehicles: Mercedes, Landrovers, a Porsche.

'If you let us in we can go and make a reservation.'

'I can't let you in if you're not a guest.'

'How can we become guests if we can't find out if there's a room?'

'It's not that kind of place, mister. You can't just come by. You have to telephone.'

'Can't you telephone?'

'No, sir. I cannot.'

'This is stupid,' said Max, putting on a pair of Ray-Bans. 'We'll be back.'

Like a man who had discovered his mission, he drove rapidly back to Desert Hot Springs and located a public telephone. Pulling out the rich man's cosh, his American Express Platinum Card, he made a brief call and within ten minutes we were back at the gate. The guard had been forewarned already and had our names off pat. 'Come right in,' he said, smiling as if we were old chums.

Afterwards, I wondered whether, if we'd been allowed in to look at the rooms, we'd actually have stayed there.

If the guard hadn't got Max into a bate, my life would have been completely different.

At first the battle of the gate seemed a pyrrhic victory. Hot Springs Ranch, it turned out, was a health spa for a strata of the brittle rich. The Capone Suite, which coincidentally was the only one vacant, was amusing enough – a bungalow stuffed with heavy mahogany furniture, big enough to accommodate Public Enemy No. 1, his moll and several cardplaying heavies. But there was no alcohol behind the long, mirrored bar and the fridge contained nothing but mineral water. It was like a redundant undertaker's parlour.

Inspection of the wider facilities revealed the spa had a restaurant, two swimming pools, tennis courts, mud baths and massage rooms, but nowhere you could pop in for a quick pint. The guests walked around wrapped in towels, or lay in the spa-pool floating on rubber rings reading scripts. Everywhere signs urged one to be quiet and respect the healing silence of the place so that it might succour the wounded souls from Hollywood.

The list of treatments read like a sushi menu: warm wraps and seaweed wraps, mud wraps, aromatherapy massages and oil massages. Max was furious to discover that they made you buy your own dressing gowns, and after supper he had had a long argument with the waiter about the kind of milk he'd like with his cup of tea. He wanted ordinary milk, but found that there was nothing on the premises that a cow would recognise. The discussion proceeded at great depth. I'd had a glass of wine and fancied a cigarette. I sneaked outside, took a wrong turning into a bush and heard someone laughing at me.

Sitting at a table outside the restaurant were two women wrapped in white towels. On the table between them was a bottle of Grand Marnier, and they were surrounded by clouds of smoke. I can't quite remember what was said at first: my eyes lit up like the jackpot on a fruit machine. I was too intent on targeting this small but vital centre of debauchery. I don't even like Grand Marnier, but under the circumstances, it was like springwater to a man dying of thirst. I quite forgot about Max and abandoned him to the battle of the full-fat.

The two women, Kim and Sam, were from Los Angeles. Sam was an actress and Kim an interior designer. Both were grievously attractive, but from the moment I saw Kim I was torn between drooling fascination and the urge to leave immediately, without waiting to pack my bags. She presented a serious threat to my simple, new life. She had cool, near-perfect, elegant looks and a languid manner that I suspected concealed a fierce personality. For a while, I paid more attention to her friend, both dreading and hoping that all this would be wrongly interpreted. I was relieved when Max emerged, grumpy, looking for me, and we were able to have a lighter, fourway discussion about the impossibility of obtaining a decent cup of tea in California. He explained that he had given up drinking and smoking and a cup of tea was now his only small pleasure in life. Sam suggested that if he wanted a natural high he should try the spa-pool. 'The water has a sedative in it,' she said. 'Lithium or something like that.'

Max was interested. 'I've been having these terrible headaches,' he said, 'and my back hurts. And I feel frightfully depressed. *And* I think there may be some-thing wrong with my head.'

'Have you tried a cranial massage?' asked Kim and the two were soon chatting about the merits of various alternative healing practices. I felt horribly jealous. He was rich and charming and handsome and flew aeroplanes and I was just the dog-man. Oh, it was rotten luck. It was all the fault of that bugger on the gate. If he'd only been polite we'd never have stayed here.

It was Sam who suggested that we went and tried the lithium pool. There was a pause; Max and I exchanged concerned glances. I could tell he was thinking the same as me, that this might well turn out to be some kind of sting. It never happens that you go to a strange and rather horrible hotel in the middle of nowhere and meet beautiful and charming women who invite you to go late-night swimming. It certainly didn't happen in England. There was a good chance they might be members of a religious cult. But they seemed all right.

'Sure,' said Kim.

'I can't swim,' said Max. 'It's odd. I can fly an aeroplane, but I can't swim.'

'I didn't know you couldn't swim,' I said. 'Is that why you wouldn't come swimming off Malibu?'

'No. It is dirty,' said Max. 'I wouldn't swim off Malibu anyway.'

Kim's face was twitching. 'You went swimming off *Malibu?*' she asked me. I was sure I could detect a note of admiration, as well as shock and perhaps disgust. 'Hey,' she said to Sam. 'Wake up. This guy went swimming off Malibu.'

Sam hiccuped. 'Freaky guy,' she said. 'There are rubber rings in the pool,' she told Max. 'It's like a hot tub. You don't have to swim. You can sleep.'

Kim tapped me on the arm. 'We'll see you both by the pool,' she said firmly, 'in a couple of minutes.'

Two days later, I called Lucy and asked her to hold on

to Parker for a little while longer as I had to stay on in Los Angeles.

'What's the matter?'

'Something's come up. It's not bad – at least I don't think so. I hope not. It's just that I've agreed to stay for a couple of days longer.'

'Hum. You don't sound all right. I think you should come back now.'

'I will soon. How's Parker?'

'Fine. Doesn't miss you at all.'

'Not one bit?'

She racked her brains. 'I suppose he has taken to sitting on the feet of strange men at bus-stops.' It was tenuous, but it would do.

'There is one problem,' Lucy said.

'Fleas, perhaps?'

'No, not fleas. That stuff I got him last time seems to have got rid of the fleas. It's his stinky whiskers.'

'Oh.'

'He keeps sniffing other dogs' mess.'

'He goes through phases of that.'

'It's a bit disgusting, you know. And I think it's given him a bad tummy. He must have caught it off all that stuff he sniffs.'

I said that I thought that dogs were pretty resistant to each others' bugs. They must be, or they'd be ill all the time.

'Or maybe it's the food I've just switched him to.' I plucked from my memory the name of some whole-meal brand.

'No,' said Lucy severely. 'We have to stop him sniffing so much.'

I told Lucy I couldn't imagine that he would be programmed to do it if it made him ill.

'But he's giving *me* a bad tummy,' she wailed.

'Then don't let him lick you.'

'But I love it when he's friendly,' my sister said. 'I want him to be affectionate. I just don't want him to be stinky.'

It sounded familiar. That incurable desire for the loved one to be all you want, without being all themselves.

From the first I told Kim that I had to go back to England: I simply had to. I could not change my flight. My plans could not be altered. My life could not be diverted. I had work to do, my flat was upside-down, my dog was waiting. I could not afford to hang around in Los Angeles just to see whether this flirtation was going to go any further. It was better if it never went any further. Just imagine, we'd be 6,000 miles apart. 'Let's just stay friends,' I urged.

On the day I was supposed to fly back, Max, relishing his grandstand view of my collapsing resolve, booked me into the Château Marmont Hotel on Sunset Boulevard. After scrutinising a few rooms, he insisted I take a wooden cottage overlooking the swimming pool. It was a faintly sinister, shady place, with a creaking door, worn 1930s furniture, and a dull patina of old grime. There were two or three bedrooms, all of which had a seedy expectant air, as if waiting for an orgy to commence. Parts of the place had just been given a slap of blue paint to cover up the remains of the last guest.

'I think you may be in luck,' said Max, casting an approving eye around. 'This may be the very place that John Belushi checked out.'

John Belushi, the actor and singer best known for *The Blues Brothers,* died of an overdose while staying at the Château Marmont in the late 1980s. He was one of numerous guests to have enjoyed the liberated atmosphere of the hotel, which remains a haven for drinkers and smokers. At some point, most of the cast-list of old Hollywood stayed here, sometimes for years. I liked the Château. It has character, the staff are democratically inclined and treat everybody in the same friendly, absent-minded and slow way. It was how I imagined old Hollywood, a bit like a prison and a bit like a palace.

I had to write a Parker column while staying at the Château Marmont. It took me most of the night, as I was disturbed by shouts of glee and splashing from the pool. In one of my rooms was a heavy desk with a leather top and a tarnished brass reading lamp. Seated in film-noir shadow, I agonised about Scottie dogs, fleas, house-training and sniffs, while from the tired carpet and brown woodwork materialised the spirits of old Hollywood screenwriters, chain-smoking cynics in sweat-stained sleeves, who had died at the desk while re-writing Roman epics and gumshoe thrillers: they hooted with laughter when they saw what I was working on. 'Listen kid,' they said. 'You complaining about having to write a column about a Scottie dog?' and they told me hard-boiled stories of life and death while from outside came the chink of glasses and bottles, as a new Hollywood generation put its feet on the primrose path.

In the early hours of the morning, Kim phoned to tell me that she'd accidentally set light to her underwear with a cigarette. She wanted to make sure I was going to be staying in Los Angeles for the lunch-date we'd arranged, and then she wanted to know when I was going to come back again. 'I can't,' I pleaded and gave her the reasons again.

'You have to come back,' she said. 'You have to meet my dogs.'

We'd sat by the spa-pool in the desert and talked about dogs and cats. She was a big dog fan and loved the sound of Parker. I'd timorously asked her for her phone number and she reeled off her home phone, office number, mobile number, pager number, fax and email address.

She had two dogs, she said, Eric and Abelard, a giant schnauzer and a Briard. She had been moving home, so they had been staying at dog-camp and I couldn't meet them. She had cats too, but they were somewhere else and one of them had suffered a trauma and was in hospital on a drip. It was a long way from Islington. It was a long way from Notting Hill.

'When you come back,' she said, 'and meet Abelard, I'd better warn you now that he does chunk people he doesn't like.'

'Chunk?'

'You know, like, take a chunk out of them. He chunked my ex.'

'I can't wait.'

'Okay, that's fixed,' she said. 'So after you come out, I'll come over and meet Parker.'

It was the dog, I thought. It was the dog that did it. And this time he wasn't even there.

10

When I returned to England, I found that Lucy had gone away for the weekend and left Parker with Foxy. 'He slept in her basket,' said Lisa, 'so she just slept on top of him.' Rather expansively, I said I'd be pleased to have Foxy to stay some time in return. I felt ambivalent when Lisa said that she might take me up on the offer, as she was going away over Christmas. If all went well, that was when Kim would be coming over, and I was worried that she might find my flat and my lifestyle a bit grim by her standards. What if we had Foxy too? Even at this hypothetical stage, life was getting complicated. I decided that if it worked out with Kim, and if she was able to put up with life in a dog-basket, then she wouldn't mind the dogs.

Parker was certainly chuffed to see his old master, if cross that I had dared to leave in the first place. For hours he stared at me until he was satisfied I was not going away, and he sniffed every item of my clothing suspiciously. I tried the usual tin of tuna that had always done the trick before, but he wasn't having any and it was two days before I woke up to find he was on the pillow and I was nearly off the bed and that things were back to normal.

He did seem to have an upset tummy, as Lucy had said, so I took him for a check-up. The vet was reassuring. 'Good, lean shape,' he said, feeling Parker. 'Ummm, nice. And claws well worn. Clean teeth. He's fine. A spot of gastro-enteritis is nothing to worry about. He's probably been dining out a bit too much.'

Probably Lucy had been spoiling him. His problem did seem to clear up and when I felt sure it was safe, I gave him a packet of Beef 'n' Mustard Frankfurter Waggoes I'd brought back from America. He tucked into these with gusto. When I woke up the next morning, he waved his left paw at me as he does when he's keen that I should be kind to him. Oh dear, there had been a little accident. Rather sweetly, he'd done it in the bathroom, next to the loo, where he'd worked out that this would be most acceptable.

'Aren't you clever?' I said, then thought how odd it was that I should feel almost pleased to see something like that.

In early winter Kensington Gardens took on the atmosphere of a sinister ballet. Under a sickle moon, silver mist hung low over the grass. Long yellow horse-chestnut leaves lay scattered like curling parchment and by the black water of the Round Pond sat thirty white swans.

Soon, night fell at tea-time. In the darkness, Parker became yet more alert to the presence of other dogs and used the shadows to practise stalking and ambush techniques he had devised. I identified three distinct types of these: the 'commando', which involved a long, crouching approach over open terrain; the 'chewing-gum', for which he flattened himself on the pavement, and the 'cotoneaster', employing the traditional dull ground cover offered by flowerbeds in the urban environment.

The success of an ambush depended to a large extent

on self-confidence. If he behaved as if he was invisible, then it was impossible that the other dog should see him. I first saw him try this out on the occasion he stalked the Westie on the South Downs outside Brighton in the summer. It was a wide green hill under a clear blue sky. Parker was like a sack of coal on a front lawn and nobody was fooled. All the same, Parker advanced on his belly, in swift darts, finally emerging from his imagined cover a few feet from the other dog, wagging his tail with delight at the success of his ruse. It is true the other dog did not move, but I can only think that it must have been mesmerised by Parker's approach, and wondered what in Dog's name he was up to.

From then on, the ambush became a favourite game. He ambushed Labradors in the country and terriers in town, he ambushed curious cats and sometimes he would ambush me. For a while, our relationship was a little like that of Inspector Clouseau played by Peter Sellers and his sidekick Cato (Burt Kwouk), who would keep him up to the mark by leaping out at him from wardrobes. I wasn't such fun as other dogs, though. Somehow, I could always see him.

One dark afternoon, we were near the corner shop at the end of Ladbroke Road, when Parker saw a Tibetan terrier being walked along the pavement. Working out that it would pass within a few feet of a motor-cycle parked on the pavement, he took cover behind the motor-cycle wheels, adopting an improvised mixture of 'chewing-gum' and 'cotoneaster'.

The Tibetan was taken quite by surprise, but immediately retaliated and the ambush became a terrier fight, which meant that for a few seconds both small dogs made terrible gnashing noises before they were separated, unscathed. I was furious with Parker, but he looked as bewildered as I was angry. I had a feeling that he hadn't expected actual violence. He had been playing at being a terrier-terrorist but the play had awoken real emotions in himself and the other dog. Perhaps in daylight, he'd have merely looked silly, but like any child, he had to realise that what was play by day caused fright at night.

He was growing up and there were inevitably occasions, mostly in the park, when he was straightforwardly aggressive, not just strutting and posing, but hating. It was all to do with scent, I'm sure, with the other dog not smelling right, but it was perplexing and at times embarrassing. He had no care for his public image, nor mine. On Hampstead Heath we met a group of polite dog-owners who said they knew about Parker and wanted to know if there was a pub nearby where they could take their dog. While I was racking my brains about where they could go for lunch, Parker tried to eat their terrier. My plea that he was aggressive only because their dog was another young male met with smiles.

'Not as friendly as you make out,' said one man, implying that he'd uncovered a journalistic scam. As they wandered off, I'm sure I heard one of the group refer to Parker as 'that horrid little dog'.

I thought about this. Had Parker been a Rottweiler in a temper, she would perhaps have called him frightening rather than horrid. There's something about a snarling small dog that provokes peculiar disdain. As with people, so with animals: we think that small men need to make a big noise and assume that small dogs also compensate.

I wondered if it was just a truism that small dogs are the most aggressive. Looking up the facts, I discovered

that dogs tend to be rated on a number of character-
istics including aggression, excitability and trainability.
Thus, the bigger dogs we think of as most dangerous
– Dobermans, Rottweilers, German shepherds – rate
high on aggression, but can be trained and are less
excitable than smaller breeds. The small dogs appear
higher up the scale of aggression because they are
much harder to train and temperamentally more excitable. The Scottie ranked fifth in the snapper stakes,
just above the Dachshund. The Westie was second
only to the Cairn terrier. Westies, apparently, have a
'very high aggression, high reactivity and only medium
trainability'. This tallied with the anecdotal evidence I
had from various vets, who told me that they'd suffered
most wounds from Westies. It certainly looked as if small
dogs were more likely to be horrid, and it was no consolation that it was not necessarily through insecurity, but
breeding. Perhaps the army should protect its bases with
packs of Westies and Cairns.

The problem was that I thought of Parker as a friendly
dog, and 99 per cent of the time this was true. He was
sweet and endearing, keen to sniff and wave his paws
at other dogs and just as keen to engage with humans.
But he was just a dog, prone to bad temper as any
other dog and I'd set him up on paper in a sensitive
anthropomorphic fashion, and thereby set us both up
for a fall.

One day I had a revelation. In Kensington Gardens we met a well-spoken woman with an ageing
Westie. Her first, drawled, sad words to me were: 'Is
yours friendly? Is he? Oh, how super. Mine isn't. He's
horrible.'

Thereafter, I realised, I didn't have to pretend that
Parker was anything but a dog, and my first words to

other people were not, 'He's friendly,' but, 'He can be horrible.'

By now, Parker had some particular enemies. There were lots of Westies around and most of them were friends with Parker. The exception was McTavish, who had become Parker's deadly foe. McTavish was really very big for his breed and as nice a dog as you could hope to meet, but he hated Parker and Parker hated him. Many times we walked around a blind corner and straight into a fracas with McTavish, as the dogs exchanged expletives, with Parker rearing on his leash and McTavish straining in his full-body harness.

McTavish's face, normally set in a benevolent, slightly anxious expression, would become contorted with emotion and he gnashed his jaws, showing huge choppers. When the two dogs spied each other across the street they made vile faces, glued their feet to the pavement and had one of those stand-offs that used to be a standard of the Spaghetti Western.

Their dislike was always heightened in the presence of Zoe, McTavish's girlfriend, a gentle, sad-eyed little Westie with fudge-coloured whiskers. She was intrigued by Parker, and would lag behind her regular squeeze in the hope of exchanging a quick sniff with this dashing, dark-haired stranger. Her flirtation caused great pain. I remember McTavish once putting his head around a corner to see where she'd got to: his expression crumbled pathetically as he caught her nose to nose with Mr P.

Among Parker's other dog-friends were the two Yorkshire terriers, Toyah and her son Rambo, belonging to Paco who ran the Sala Nova hairdressers on Ladbroke Road. Rambo was the runt of the litter and had remained a tiny dog with a big character, who looked like a furiously barking moustache. Though he and Parker never fought, they vied for possession of the pavement outside Paco's salon, marking and remarking the bollards and flowerpots, and Rambo valiantly defended his mother from Parker's attentions.

Rambo's big heart gave way one day when he was attacked by a Staffie in Ladbroke Grove. He died of shock in Paco's arms. Paco got another little Yorkie, called Oscar, who was sweet, but for a while Toyah went into a depression and could barely be coaxed from her basket.

A second trip to Los Angeles went off well, rather too well. Abelard did not 'chunk' me and we became the best of friends after he realised that I was more fond of walking than Kim was. It became inevitable that Kim would come over to England. As Christmas approached I made a few changes to the flat which I thought would improve it, like getting rid of the old sofa and bed. At first I tried to have them collected by the council but rubbish is big business nowadays and I was told I'd have to fill in a form, then a man would come down and see what there was to take away, then I'd get a price. But nothing could be done for a week, because they were too busy.

So I took the time-honoured route and stuck the bed and sofa out on the street in the hope that someone would give them a new home. The bed went out on the Portobello in the late afternoon. It was still there at twilight but the moment night fell, it vanished. I didn't see who took it. One moment it was there, a big old bed with a big old mattress, the next it had gone.

I was encouraged. Somewhere out in the darkness

was a big hungry furniture-eating creature. I put out some more food for it the next afternoon, but the sofa proved less tempting, though I stuck a note on it saying *Please take me.*

Several times I walked Parker past his old friend. Once, he hopped on the sofa, curled up and began to settle down for the night. Later, Lucy whistled up from the street to point out that the sofa had been placed across the bonnet of my Landrover. Perhaps it had climbed up there.

As the night went on, the sofa became a focus for all sorts of drama that I couldn't help but overhear. Girls sat and complained about boys, boys gathered and complained about girls. A gaggle of homesick Australians talked about cricket. In the small hours, two drunks tried to carry the sofa away, but had to give up after a few yards. One went to sleep on it.

I went to bed feeling sorry for the old green sofa that no one wanted. The ridiculous consequence of writing about Parker was that, these days, I could be anthropomorphic about almost anything. Perhaps I'd have to break it up and take it to the dump down in Chelsea.

The next morning I was woken up by a terrible crunching noise, like a giant tucking into a bowl of giant-sized cornflakes. Looking out of the window I saw that I'd been right about there being a furniture-eating animal. The green sofa was dangling from a pair of huge metal jaws. I invited Parker to take a look, and he watched curiously and to my mind, a little sadly, as his smelly old friend disappeared down the road for ever, swallowed up by a hungry refuse cart.

In mid-December, Parker returned from a walk with

Lucy to find a large pile of half-unpacked clothing on the floor. He was tired and naturally assumed that the clothes had been thoughtfully placed there for his benefit. He lay down and passed into a deep sleep, from which he was waked by the sound of a woman saying 'So you like cashmere, do you?'

Kim had a lot of cashmere. She liked being spoiled and was a terrible spoiler herself. She spoiled Parker rotten, giving him an old silk blanket to lie on and feeding him slices of roast turkey from the delica- tessen Mr Christians on Elgin Crescent. A look of profound greed, that I'd never before seen, came into Parker's eyes. They loved Kim at Mr Christians as they came to love her up and down the arcades on the Portobello Road.

Kim had decided that she would justify being in England by buying 'a few pieces' of antique furniture for her store in Los Angeles. This sounded to me like a pleasant enough way to spend a week or so, but I'd misunderstood the scale of the operation she had stealthily planned and Parker and I found ourselves caught up in the business of buying enough stuff to fill a 40-foot container. For several weeks I was in a whirlwind of emotion, in love and in chaos, flying around with all the other debris, the mahogany tables and walnut chairs, pine dressers, oak chests, mirrors, lamps, knick-knacks and old silk fabric that filled my flat so that there was no room to sit down because of the furniture. Oh, it was all the fault of that guard on the gate at the Hot Springs Ranch!

People do lay great store by how their pets react to partners. Mostly it's so that in retrospect they can say: 'I knew that he/she was no good anyway when Rufus bit him/her the first time they met.' Parker was confused. The cashmere was a great improvement, the fridge was full of treats and when I was out of the room, he'd hop on Kim's lap, slipping off when I returned and hiding in a corner – if he could find an empty one – where he gave the appearance of sulking. If I pretended to go out, and instead crept back in, I'd catch him with his head on her lap again. I wasn't sure whether it was jealousy or loyalty, whether he wanted her to stay or could not altogether relinquish the idea of one-dog-and-his-man.

Kim loved Mr P. She was amused when the odd person recognised him. Los Angeles revolved around a culture of celebrity, so it struck her as funny that in England a dog should be more recognisable than its owner. Sometimes, I couldn't help wishing that some of Parker's celebrity would rub off on me, and that I'd be recognised for myself, as more than just the man behind the dog.

One evening in December, we were scuttling through the gloom to the off-licence on Elgin Crescent, Parker snuffling behind us like a small Hoover, when I was recognised by a girl sitting outside the Duke of Wellington. There's a bench on the corner where people hide from the rain and eat fish and chips from the Fish Pond on the Portobello. (I've always thought the Fish Pond an odd name for a chippie, evoking pond fish floating belly-up in water the colour of tea, full of old bicycles and supermarket trolleys.) Unusually, the girl with the chips didn't say 'There's Parker,' but asked me if I was 'the *Telegraph* man with the dog'.

The girl had a friend with her, who was shocked. 'You don't read the *Telegraph*?' she asked.

'I read about Parker,' said the first girl.

'Ho, ho,' laughed the friend. 'Ho. Ho. Ughh.' Then

she began shouting at me. 'Oi, *Telegraph* man, bit right-wing. Move to the right. Bit right-wing. Move to the right. Bit right-wing.'

I dragged Kim into the off-licence, which as it happened entailed a turn to the right.

'Bit right-wing, turn to the right,' came the shouts. 'Poor Parker with his Fascist master.'

Kim did not understand. I explained that some people considered the *Daily Telegraph* to be a bastion of conservative opinion, though this tradition now survived largely in the occasional forthright leader article. Of course it was unjust that these scribblers should remain anonymous while the writer of a dog-column was barracked, but it was all meant in a good spirit. There were many young people who read the *Telegraph* on the sly: I knew a girl with impeccable liberal-left credentials who told me that she put on Marigold gloves to retrieve the paper from her parents' dustbin.

Shortly afterwards, an opportunity arose, so I thought, for me to improve my personal profile without risking a direct confrontation with the public, when Trinnie Woodall and Susannah Constantine asked if Parker could model winter-wear for the *Telegraph Weekend Section*. I hoped that the shoot would include both of us, and I'd walk away with full-page exposure and a bag-full from Paul Smith.

I took Parker to be groomed and even had a shave myself before arriving more early than bright for the shoot in Battersea, only to be let down when Trinnie said that they were 'going to do babies first, and then we'll be doing the dogs, so if you'd like to leave Parker here I can drop him off later'.

They just wanted Parker, so I'd once again have to

settle for greatness by association. Kim and I lingered as dressers to the star.

I'd never seen the point of dog-coats. But Parker did look striking in an orange suede coat lined with lambswool, as if his pedigree had been underlined by conspicuous material comfort. He seemed to like the coat and made no attempt to shake it off: with his big whiskers and short haircut, I fancied he looked like a dashing pilot in a flying jacket.

While they 'did babies' we took Parker to Battersea Park. It was a damp, mild morning, and the park was empty but for hunched peacocks and a few hatchet-faced men in shellsuits staring greedily at the moorhens bobbing on the lake. The dead calm was in contrast to the chaos in the studio on our return. Other dogs had arrived to be photographed and the place became a mêlée of models and assistants, babies, nannies, photographers, work experience girls, dogs donning clothes and humans taking them off.

A dozen mobile phones were ringing and from the corner came the hum of a generator: this transpired to be an expressor for breast-milk. To cap it all, one of the other guest dogs was a spaniel called Ziggy, who Parker had several times fought for possession of the trees on Chepstow Villas. Some celebrity bad-temper ensued: as Parker's manager, I spoke harshly to him after which he sulked behind a stack of screens in a corner. When it came to his turn to be photographed he used the screens as his dressing room and would retreat to be alone between takes.

We bought Parker the little suede coat. When I spoke to a colleague at the *Telegraph* and said how impressive Parker looked in suede, he agreed and said the photographs had come out well.

'He's so cool,' he sniggered. 'He looks just like a rich bookie.'

This wasn't what I wanted to hear. I had imagined Parker a hero when others saw him as a spiv. To test public opinion, I put Parker's coat on him and took him for a walk along Westbourne Grove. Three girls descended on us. 'What a cute coat,' one cooed. They began looking at the label and asking where the coat came from and how much it cost. The dog inside became of secondary importance and Parker stood miserably, whiskers sinking, quite overshadowed by his clothes, just like any other fashion victim.

My uneasiness about celebrity status was compounded by a dawn visit to Bermondsey antiques market when I was berated by a poodle-owner. 'I knew you when you used to walk around Islington,' he sneered. 'Oh, but now you're in West London you don't think a lot of Islington, do you?'

I wasn't sure whether he was talking to Parker or me. I couldn't remember having said a bad word about Islington and Parker was heartbroken to leave the North London lamp-posts. I was confused and upset. Perhaps people didn't like to see a dog making good. The coat went on a hook behind the door. Parker would not wear it until I was feeling a little more secure.

Just before Christmas, we went to Lincolnshire to visit my parents. For Parker, this was dog-heaven. My parents then had three old spaniels – Thomas, Lily and Rosie – who formed a heaving, smelly, barking carpet. The well-being of her dogs has always been of paramount importance to my mother and Parker happily fell into the routine of walks, biscuits and barking. It did take a while for him to be accepted, because spaniels tend to be jealous, and he also had to suffer the pangs of an unsatisfied infatuation for Lily. He was persistent, though, and when they had stopped barking at him and were nodding off he would sneak closer and closer until he could go to sleep with his head on a spaniel's bum.

Lincolnshire was superb rabbiting countryside, too. Where my parents lived on the Wolds, the long, gently sloping hills offered fine vantage points and encouraged a good rate of acceleration for the chase. Parker caught the odd rabbit, though they were mostly diseased, and the transformation from jovial Scottie to slavering killer was a revelation. He was always pleased as punch afterwards. There were also three or four cats around the house, most of whom did not mind being chased for fun.

Parker had just returned to London and was admiring his Christmas cards, many of them showing a pair of Scotties staring out of the window at a snowy landscape, when Foxy bounced in the door and sat on him.

I had forgotten that Foxy was coming to stay. Lisa told us she was in fine form. She'd been recently left for a weekend with Lorraine who worked at Food on the Hill, and had eaten an alarm clock. She had also attempted to ambush another dog by jumping from the roof of the café and had eaten a packet of Nurofen painkillers stolen from a handbag, enough to put out your average human. On her, they had no effect whatsoever.

Foxy was thrilled to have Parker to herself. Just imagine: four days of whisker biting! Straight away, she attempted to mount him. Parker extricated himself and went and hid in a very small, dark space under the bed where there used to be a drawer. He liked her all right, but he hadn't counted on her moving in. Over Christmas, his face took on a look of abject self-pity and his shoulders sagged with the burden of the unhappy domestic arrangement. He would barely condescend to sniff Foxy's bottom. She was perplexed and tried furiously to get a rise out of him, but he just turned his back on her and sighed. He used to run jealously to protect her when she flirted with other dogs in the park: now he stared, shrugged, and went back to sniffing.

Just as she tried to assert her dominance over Parker, so Foxy engaged me in a battle for authority. She peed on my bed, stole a ball from a Labrador in the park, chased the geese by the lake and tried to snatch a doughnut from my hand. On the lead, she dragged so hard she almost choked herself and her death rattles earned me accusations of cruelty from every sentimental drunk: off the lead, she tried to encourage Parker to play with the traffic. When reprimanded she grovelled in mock abasement verging on mockery. She knew I was a temporary master and a soft touch.

What really upset Parker was the way she would try to be first back into the flat. It had become a routine that he followed me in the communal door, then ran up the stairs ahead of me, waiting on the landing to offer a smelly lick. Foxy's insistence on being first up the stairs seemed to depress him more than anything.

We had to sort things out. I'm not sure what happened, but Kim said that one dark midnight she saw me 'taking the dogs for a walk' clutching a half-bottle of whisky. When I came back, the bottle was empty and Foxy slunk into her basket when she was told.

As far as I remember, I wasn't beastly to Foxy, but somehow I got her to walk behind Parker, and once she realised that he was top dog, things became better. He still wouldn't speak to her, but she did lay off his whiskers and waited for him to go into the flat first and didn't try to eat his food. His good temper returned, slowly, and by the fourth day they were playing together, tugging at a toy. I wished Parker could have sorted it out himself. Confronted by another male, he would address the question of authority straight away, but he was a coward with a bossy girl.

By the time Foxy went back to Lisa, she was showing signs of sexual confusion. I saw her look at Parker cock his leg on a tree, contemplate squatting, then cock her own leg.

In the quest for antiques, Kim, Parker and I travelled all over the South of England, visiting markets and auction houses and warehouses. Parker diligently sniffed the pad-feet and splayed-feet of hundreds of antique tables and chests. In some shops they gave him biscuits: in others he met fierce dogs. In Oxfordshire he sniffed the legs of a dealer who only that day had lost his own dog; it was sad to see Parker looking for an animal that had died only hours before. There were hundreds of ancient smells to be chronicled: a Georgian commode, adapted as a drinks cabinet, gave him much to think about.

Over New Year we went to Cornwall and Devon, where the weather was so bad that Parker's walks were severely curtailed. In North Cornwall the waves rolled up to the steps of the Tate Gallery at St Ives, while along the coast the wind was so strong that it was hard to stand upright. The sea frothed furiously, dark green like old bacon streaked with white fat, the rain poured down and our car shuddered ominously on the cliff-tops.

In Devon we stayed at the Thurlestone Hotel, over-looking the sea, which allowed dogs in some of the standard rooms. Because of some odd pricing arrangement, it cost us only a few pounds more to take a deluxe room for ourselves, leaving Parker in his permitted standard suite. He didn't stay there: we smuggled him down the corridor to help out with supper, concealing him whenever a member of staff knocked on the door. The food was excellent, but I could tell that Parker would have traded his share of the breast of partridge for a decent muddy walk.

As the shopping went on, home-life became impossible. My kitchen was full of glass fruit and the floors shimmered with expensive mirrors. Parker showed his adaptability in sleeping on a pile of iron chandeliers but it was harder for the humans. One night, I got into bed and stubbed my toe on an Italian pineapple-shaped wall sconce that had slunk between the blankets. Work was impossible: sleep was impossible. For Kim's last few days we moved to the Portobello Hotel. It had no stated policy on dogs, but no one seemed to care whether a Scottie dog was bunking down there or not. Apart from the stay at Thurlestone, we'd lived mostly off sandwiches, and decided to treat ourselves to a meal at Leith's Restaurant. To my surprise, when I telephoned to make a reservation and gave my name I was asked if Parker would be joining us.

Here at last was the benefit of being a celebrity dog. Not recognition, or pictures, or gossip but the chance to go out together for a feast. As a last thought, I dressed Parker in his much derided suede jacket. When he pottered into Leith's, wagging his tail, relaxed and cheerful as if *he* were taking *us* out, the manager offered to hang up his coat and, showing him to a discreet booth, whispered that when the opportunity presented itself, he'd be delighted to take Parker outside and give him a nibble.

It was a triumphant night for Parker. He had a

bit of beef to take away and went to sleep, between two teddies we bought in Devon, with his feet up, like a little black bear, famous for a night and loving it.

11

One of the consequences of having a transatlantic relationship was insomnia. Late-night telephone calls kept me up until well after midnight. I'd always been a night-worker anyway, who enjoyed the time after everyone else had gone to bed, and what with the telephone calls and thinking about the strange direction of my life, I often found myself walking Parker at two in the morning.

We rarely saw any other dogs at that time, though there was the occasional muffled bark from a shuttered household, so I let him off the lead to plod behind me. The wintry West London nights were clear and cold, the bare plane trees covered in slippery grey moonlight. I would hear nothing but Parker's claws clicking along the pavement: his sniffing sounded enormous, as if there was a giant dog following behind me.

One night, we saw a ghost-dog. It passed us on Denbigh Terrace, a short street running off the Portobello with a terrace of houses on one side and a council estate on the other. The ghost turned the corner onto Denbigh Road and vanished. I couldn't see the dog very well, but I could make out that it was brown and white and seemed to be hobbling. Parker looked at it but – strangely – made no effort to investigate further. Thinking the dog might be a stray I followed it around the corner, but found only an empty pavement. I reckoned that it probably knew its way around so well that its owners let it out to take a leak under its own steam. It must have gone back into a doorway further along.

A week or so later, we were out again at about two in the morning, walking on Denbigh Terrace. Parker was dawdling and I called for him to catch up. When he didn't come, I turned round and saw that he was transfixed by the sight of a dog that was trundling towards us.

It was the same dog. This time I could see it more clearly. It was an old, fluffy thing, a cross between a Jack Russell and a hamster, hopping along on three good legs and one stiff one. It had a collar on, and looked cared for. It moved steadily and intently past us, sniffing at the wall bordering the council estate, snuffled around the corner into Denbigh Road and vanished.

I know it vanished, because this time I took a closer look at the road and saw that there were no front doors, only the locked iron gates of the estate and beyond that a strip of Westbourne Grove, lit up by yellow street-lamps. Looking back at the route the dog had followed, I couldn't see an open gate either. Where had the dog come from and where had it gone to?

Parker's reaction was interesting. The dog passed within a few feet of him, but he made no attempt to sniff it: he simply watched it trot on its way, with his head cocked quizzically. Perhaps it was the other dog's absolute concentration that put him off, or perhaps, as human ghosts cast no shadow, so this phantom dog had no smell.

Phantom dogs are traditionally malign creatures, the shape taken by devils. There are also dog-ghosts who howl on their masters' graves, canine spectres whose behaviour is connected to their relationships with humans, but I don't think I've ever come across a dog-ghost that just went about its independent dog-life. Of course it couldn't really have been a spook, but the thought that it might have been was quite cheering. I once saw a distressing cartoon of two dogs in Heaven, lamenting that they weren't allowed to sniff bottoms. Perhaps this was a good dog that couldn't bear to leave its favourite smells, and was allowed to walk them nightly, without any human pestering it to hurry up, until the end of time.

The ghostly Jack Russell might have been a portent, for shortly after its appearance, Lucy acquired a living, breathing Jack Russell that was to blight Parker's quiet life.

It wasn't that Parker had anything against Jack Russells. In fact, the only breed he seemed to dislike on principle were Cavalier King Charles Spaniels. I once made some flippant joke in the column about this and was inundated with furious responses from spaniels, most beginning with, 'Grr, grr, grr.' One of them referred to me as 'that pig'. Some of these small dogs were snooty about their Stuart pedigree. I didn't bother to remind them that Charles I preferred the greyhound to the spaniel, and that they owed their 'royal' title to the affection of Charles II, who liked to stroke a small dog in times of stress. This habit annoyed Samuel Pepys who wrote testily of 'the silliness of the King, playing with his dog all the while, or his codpiece, and not minding the business, and what he said was mighty weak'. Cavalier King Charles Spaniels seemed to reciprocate Parker's animosity. There were a lot of them around Kensington and he was constantly barracked from the open windows of houses and cars. I put this mutual dislike down to the failed campaigns of Charles I against the Scots, which led ultimately to his demise.

Subsequently, terriers became the court favourites, so the spaniels may well bear a grudge.

Anyway, one day we came back from a few days in the country and found a Jack Russell at the top of the stairs. He had a huge brown head with a long thin nose, a round little body and quick, worried eyes, which were looking crossly at the new arrival. 'He's called Brock,' Lucy told us. Brock was not pleased to see Parker. He growled. Parker went and hid under my bed.

I was surprised by Brock. Lucy had talked about getting a dog, which I encouraged because I thought Parker would appreciate the company, especially if it was a nice girlie dog. I was anxious that he should find a girlfriend. Then she'd changed her mind because her boyfriend Thanassi didn't want one. Then she'd decided that she would get one anyway, 'A little miniature dachshund, oh I saw the sweetest one today,' and then she'd said she'd wait. Now there was Brock, who Thanassi had chosen. Brock had some 'form' too and had been through several owners.

'You were going to get a miniature dachshund,' I said to Lucy.

'He's got dachshund in him.'

Parker emerged tentatively and Brock jumped on his neck, making terrible terrier noises.

'Oh dear,' I said. 'Two males will be a problem. Is he going to be neutered?'

'He is already,' said Lucy. 'His last owner had him done because he shagged everything in sight. Hasn't stopped him, has it, Brockie?'

She gazed adoringly at the little dog, who wagged his tail, hopped on her lap and stared defiantly at Parker, baring his teeth as if to say, 'Keep off my gravy train.'

Brock proved to be a handful, jealous and feisty with

a habit of attacking men in leather trousers, but he was also a dear and clever little dog. Within days he had learned to beg and roll over in exchange for treats. He had wonderful eyesight and lightning reactions. He could see a crumb fall from the table at five yards and catch it before it hit the floor. His little tummy, anxious to know that it would always be filled, kept him scouting constantly for scraps and he was a frequent visitor to my untidy kitchen area, where Parker scattered the boring bits of his previous nights supper. Sometimes Brock forgot himself and played tug-of-war with Parker, but mostly he hated him. He hated Parker because Lucy stroked Parker and on these trips to my flat Brock would invariably cock his leg on something or other, trying to erase the smell of that other dog that threatened his comfortable new life.

Sometimes I complained about the pee to Lucy and Thanassi; sometimes I overlooked the matter.

'Don't you ever get really sick of Parker?' Lucy asked me one day. 'I mean, are there days when you just can't cope?'

The two dogs were sniffing each other cautiously. Brock hadn't seen Parker for a few days and had evidently hoped that was the last of him. He put his head on Parker's neck and growled, with the hairs on his back bristling like a hairbrush. Parker sighed and lay down. Brock trotted off and did something in a corner. His tiny little legs moved rapidly and gave everything he did a slightly hurried, shifty look. You couldn't help noticing him, especially when he was trying not to be noticed.

I pretended not to see. 'Of course,' I said. 'It's quite natural to have a battle with your pet.'

Lucy looked relieved. 'He's the sweetest dog,' she

said, 'and we love him but sometimes he can be very demanding. We can't leave him alone or he starts shaking. I know it's to do with his background and everything, but it is tiring. Then there's the people he attacks. This leather trousers business.'

'And the peeing in my flat.'

She nodded quickly. 'Oh yes, and that too. Oh dear. One more thing.'

Brock sat at her feet and pulled a tragic face, his ears flopping in misery.

'Oh Brockie,' Lucy said guiltily. 'I'm so sorry.'

Immediately, the dog perked up and hopped on her lap. Parker watched impassively, as if he'd seen it all before.

'If he's naughty I don't know what to do to punish him,' said Lucy. 'How do you punish Parker?'

'I have smacked him. I once smacked him when he bit me as a puppy: I had been telling him off for rootling in the dustbin. Otherwise I've just spoken severely to him. Occasionally I deprive him of his favourite things, by walking him on a lead and refusing to let him sniff. He hates that.'

It was pretty arbitrary, not like any of the dog-training books, but I tended to the opinion that those who have a well-constructed system of rewards and punishments are more interested in the process than the pooch. Besides, any system is liable to hypocrisy, and I think a dog can work this out as well as any human.

I'd been no help to Lucy and she took Brock off for his dinner. After she'd gone I examined the corner I'd seen Brock in and found a dribble of pee on the floor. It was partly out of curiosity that I mentioned this little accident to Lucy and Thanassi. I wondered what strategy of punishment or persuasion they had settled for. Would they put his nose in his own scent, or just speak to him?

The response was unexpected. 'We've decided,' said Lucy, 'that it isn't Brock peeing in your flat. It's Parker.'

They sat on their sofa, a study in a burgeoning family unit, flanked by their cats and with Brock sitting perkily on his mother's lap. Unable to discipline their beloved, they had side-stepped the issue and opted instead for the strategy of parental denial.

I was always reading literature that told me how good for one's health and family pets are. Considered alongside the episode of Max's grey squirrel, this incident made me realise how handy it is to have someone else's dog about the place to pick up the blame for those unexplained little accidents.

For a while I toyed with the idea of retaliation. Parker would have to pee in their flat, and if he wouldn't I would do it for him. I never got around to pursuing this and after a bit, Brock seemed to stop the habit of his own accord. There was an interlude of peace, then the raiding expeditions began.

I noticed that a number of Parker's toys – a squeaky sheep thing from America, a cricket ball, an old marrow bone – were missing. My suspicions were confirmed when I saw Brock slink into the flat ostensibly searching for crumbs, and remove a dog-chew that Lucy had given Parker a few days before. He went about the burglary on tiptoe, casting frequent apprehensive looks in my direction. Parker, apparently asleep on a pile of old newspapers, nonetheless had a beady eye open and pinned on the Jack Russell, but did nothing to stop him. Upstairs a large stash of contraband was discovered, and Brock's parents shook their heads and said they didn't know what to do with him.

'Perhaps you could try some sessions with a trainer,' I said.

'What – call in the Social?' said Thanassi. 'No way.'

Brock's greed supplied its own punishment. He didn't have much holding capacity for the food he consumed and on walks, he was a 'three-bag dog'. One night, I heard Lucy out in the street shouting desperately for him. She'd let him downstairs to go for a walk and he'd shot out of the front door and hoofed it up the street into the night. He was discovered some way off crouched against a tree, in considerable agony. Back in the flat, the missing piece of the story turned up in the shape of a torn wrapper from a family-sized bar of Cadbury's fruit and nut. Brock had snaffled it from the table and had eaten the whole lot.

Parker's refuge from everything became my parents' house in Lincolnshire. It was here that I now left him when I had to go away, and he always had a lovely time. There were other animals besides his spaniel friends, Thomas, Lily and Rosie. For a while there was Mr Floppy the rabbit, who lived in the hen run, but he was killed by a dog from next door. His place was taken by Eric the pheasant, who wandered in half-starved and soon turned chicken, rootling with the others. At nights Eric slept in a patch of nettles. The hen run was a nice warm spot in the spring sunshine. Sometimes my mother fell asleep there.

There was an ever-changing population of cats around the house. One of the oldest and nicest, Minnie, died that year: she was found in a flowerbed, and Ginger Plumpkin, who had adopted my parents, was run over. Their places were taken by two black cats, Tabatha Twitchit and Penny, both cast-offs from other family members. Tabatha was a small, sleek kleptomaniac, who sat much of the day under a side-lamp in the kitchen, warming herself, and watching for the butter to be left unattended. She struck back at anyone who shooed her from the table, hitting their shins with her paws. Penny talked a lot and at first spent most of her time hiding in the cellars.

Parker adapted easily to life there. One of the things I do know about country life is that you must have a strict regime, or you can slump into a kind of gentle rural seediness, which you mistake for relaxation but which leads to existential panic. People who move to the country, tempted by beauty experienced on holiday or remembered from childhood, can be shocked to find how cold and unresponsive the natural gods become when you're their neighbours. For most people natural beauty is a good backdrop but not in itself sufficient company.

Parker seemed to know this too, for he set himself a strict round of duties. In the morning he went around the bedrooms waking up all the lazybones humans, then he spent a few hours methodically marking the garden. After a nap, he would sit on the doorstep to guard the house. Hunched into a stance that evoked Geoffrey Boycott facing Andy Roberts, he snapped at flies or sniffed the breeze blowing from a neighbouring farm where there was a pair of Labrador bitches. Sometimes, seeing him sitting there I realised what a grown-up dog he'd become. His bottom no longer wobbled. He was an exceptionally long-nosed, stinky-whiskered, handsome Scot.

My parents' friends were all doggy-folk and intrigued by Parker. It was generally agreed that 'you don't see many of them nowadays' and several locals 'always had a Scottie when they were children'. One woman told my mother that her family had had a pair of Scotties when she was growing up. She used to dress them up in skirts and bonnets and push them around in a pram. They bit her, but she persisted. I don't know what it is about Scotties, but they do seem to bring out the mothering instinct, for I'd heard similar confessions from other people. I came across a fine example of this species of anecdote in Cecil Aldin's book of sketches entitled *Dogs of Character* (1927), in which he tells the story of Bogie, a Scottie bitch that belonged to a three-year-old girl whose family lived near Hyde Park. The girl liked to dress up the Scottie 'in the flowing robes of a large baby doll', its paws pushed through the armholes, head covered with a tightly tied baby's bonnet. Bogie was then put in a perambulator and taken for walks.

Bogie had an instinct for a warm, secure sleeping place, and did not object. The only thing she liked more than a snooze was a scrap. One day, her mistress was pushing Bogie through Hyde Park in the perambulator, when they arrived in the middle of a dog-fight. A collie and a bull terrier were at each other. Several policemen had become involved, whacking at the dogs with sticks without success, and injuries were expected all round. 'Suddenly,' Aldin writes, 'from the snowy depths of the perambulator burst a black and hairy-faced baby' who scurried into the fray on all fours, barking furiously, trailing behind her the flowing infant's dress, which she constantly tripped over. Terrified by this apparition, the other dogs let go of each other and bolted, leaving Bogie in her bonnet, tail quivering with excitement, victor of the field.

Dogs of Character also had a picture of a Scottie called Nonie, a war-dog, born on board HMS *Lion* during the

Battle of Jutland. His owner was a colonel in the Royal Flying Corps and the dog joined him on bombing raids across German lines. Nonie flew the Channel and later rode into battle in a tank. His various 'medals' were inscribed on his name-tag. The drawing of Nonie showed him lying in an attitude I recognised from Parker, like a sleepy bear, with melancholy eyes dominating a phlegmatic expression.

Dogs of Character was one of a few doggy books I'd picked up while I'd had Parker. Although I professed not to be that kind of mad dog-owner, I always kept an eye out for literature that could help me understand more about my strange relationship with Parker. I'd already discovered I wasn't the first Scottie diarist, for a kind reader had sent me a copy of *Mr Rhoddie Dhu*, one of several gently humorous Scottie journals written by C. B. Poulteney in the 1930s. Mr Dhu was a decent fellow, who said, 'Hoots,' and who had an endearing affection for Pat the black cat. Though Parker was a child of his time and less innocent, there was much about Mr Dhu that I recognised in him, notably his stubbornness, curiosity and cheek.

I was envious of Mr Dhu's powers of speech. I wished Parker could talk, as it would have been a help with the column, but I'd never found a voice for him. In any case, the definitive terrier voice had been done already by Kipling in *Thy Servant, A Dog* (1930). The 'wonderful and dretful' story of the terriers Boots and Slippers and their hound-friend Ravager, it sustains a perfectly realised dog-language, a semi-articulate mangled syntax that generates heart-wrenching pathos. Any voice I imagined for Parker always ended up seeming human nonsense by comparison.

At the *Telegraph* I was by now on the index cards of

various departments as a dog-specialist, and anything that smacked of pets or anthropomorphism was sent my way. One day, I was asked to interview the American novelist Paul Auster, who had written a small novel called *Timbuktu*, the story of Mr Bones, a tragic mutt condemned to a wandering life after his eccentric and irresponsible master had passed away. I thought Auster a wonderful writer. Though Mr Bones never actually spoke, the liberty and humour with which Auster portrayed the consciousness of the animal was inspiring.

Parker first spoke to me on a spring afternoon in Highgate Woods. It came about because of his fear of footballs. He had lost all enthusiasm for the game after his bum was whacked by a football in Kensington Gardens. He had been browsing the edge of the pretty flowerbeds by the Bayswater entrance like some big black bumble bee, inhaling the rich mixture of mulch and other-dogs, near a group of children who were having their first stab at the national shame, when suddenly a big white football struck Parker's big black bottom.

It was a dreadful shock and doubly perturbing because the missile that had hit him kept moving, looking as if it might at any moment make a second attack. Rolling his eyes heavenwards, Parker scuttled off, to the accompaniment of cruel laughter from children who hadn't intended to hurt, but were not altogether unsatisfied with the results. The event left its scars and Parker developed a keen eye for a football. He understood the potential of the shape even when it was not in motion, and many times I saw him retreat in horror from pedestrians who were only holding the malevolent spheres.

In Highgate Woods, Parker was having a lovely time until we came to the playing fields, where he suddenly vanished. I found him sitting behind a beech tree, occasionally poking his nose around the corner and casting one huge, piteous brown eye in the direction of the field, where a dozen impromptu games of football were in progress.

'Come on,' I said. 'Don't be silly. You're quite safe with me.'

'Pull the other one,' his look seemed to say. 'I'd sooner have a bath than go out there. You don't know what it's like.'

'As a matter of fact, I do know what it's like,' I said. 'When I was a fat little bookworm, the school playground was full of horrors.'

Suddenly we were having a dialogue.

'These little oiks laugh when they hit me,' he said. 'And I can't tell them to get stuffed. At least if you're the same species you can tell them to leave you alone.'

'It doesn't work that way,' I explained. 'A child responding to his persecutors is a red rag to a bull.'

The simile made no sense to the dog. I cast around for a canine equivalent. 'There's no reason for it,' I said. 'Small people are horrid to each other. It's instinctive. Like when you see Ziggy peeing on your tree.' Ziggy was the spaniel who shared Parker's territory around the Portobello: they did the photo shoot for Trinnie and Susannah, the day Parker got the suede coat.

Parker didn't care for the suggestion that he might be a bit of a bully, and was about to argue that these territorial disputes were undertaken in my interest as well, but before we could go on, I realised that my Dr Dolittle antics were attracting too much attention, so we wandered back through the woods. Away from the footballers, Parker was in happy, galloping mode. He made several new friends, large and small, and was deeply impressed by a huge German mountain dog that towered above him like King Kong above Fay Wray, though the sexes were reversed. The confidence with which he approached this dog puzzled me.

'Parker,' I whispered, looking around to make sure there were no psychiatrists lurking in the bushes, North London being their natural environment. 'Parker, how is it that you know some big dogs are okay and others are not to be messed with? Even if they're bitches. I mean, you'll give Rottweilers and Doberman bitches a wide berth. May I ask you about the mysteries of your nose?'

He looked at me, red tongue lolling, happily uncomprehending, and I realised that he couldn't understand a word I was saying. It hit me that the Dolittle thing was the wrong way round. I couldn't speak to him, but he could definitely communicate with me. Only, he was going to be at his most articulate when he was most needy: when he was happy, he hadn't got a thing to say for himself.

I had this insight confirmed when a few weeks later I discovered Parker's secret diary. I was going through a pile of crumpled paper under my desk when I came across a sheet of A4 ripped from the pad, as if by teeth, and covered with writing that looked as if I might have attempted it with my left hand using an old, splayed felt-tip.

Sunday, I read. *Eventually taken for walk with Brock. He tried to stop me sniffing and make me chase him. I told him I would bite his bum. He laughed and told me I wouldn't dare.*

Monday. Late-night encounter with McTavish, giant Westie from round the corner, six foot tall with metal teeth and daggers for claws, so understandable caution on my part. Fortunately, he was wearing his restraining harness. In Chepstow Villas, encountered Unknown Yorkie, peeing on third tree down. Grr. Grr.

And so it went on. I was surprised by his version of our life together. There was no mention of the two trips that week to Hampstead Heath, nor of the bacon sandwich he had scoffed on Monday, nor the attention and affection lavished on him. It was just dogs, dogs, dogs and an endless adolescent account of uncertainties, aggression and infatuation, which didn't tally with my perception of him as a confident pooch, the 'horrible little dog' of Hampstead Heath.

Thursday. Given bone. Buried bone in big bed. (Ha! I thought, is he referring to **my** bed?) *Met girlie Scottie called Molly. She quite liked my side-step and roll but not that interested in sniffs. When, oh when, will I find some like-minded dog? Brock came downstairs and ate my biscuits. I told him I would bite his bum. He laughed. Yesterday it rained, so much work to be done reconstructing territorial perimeters. Chased big Doberman in park, so know that my restraint with Brock is courtesy not cowardice.*

This was not strictly true. We met a Doberman puppy and Parker, who usually stays well clear of Dobermans, took the opportunity to bully a good-natured dog younger than himself. All the same, I was troubled to think of the pain my dog was going through in his attempts to assert himself with Brock. Friday's entry revealed that he had at last faced up to some fears.

In park with Brock and he peed on a good sniff I had found. I remembered I had seen off a Doberman the day before, and a Jack Russell was nothing, so I bit his bum. Brock was very surprised. 'What did you do that for?' he said. 'Because I told you I was going to,' I said, 'and I'll do it again.' He laughed, so I bit his bum again. He squeaked. I laughed.

I felt I had to speak to Parker. I found him on the armchair, cleaning his privates.

'Parker,' I said. 'Did you write this?'

'If you say so,' he replied.

'I'm sorry for reading it,' I said, 'but I was worried. I had no idea you were having such a hard time. Why don't you talk to me about it?'

He licked his whiskers. 'Well, it's a dog's life growing up,' he said. 'You probably can't remember. And you ought not to read my diary. Like any adult scavenging through their kid's waste-paper bin, you wanted to see what I thought of you.'

'You don't mention me at all,' I blurted.

'You ought to be pleased,' he said. 'There's an old canine saying: "A happy dog thinks nothing of its master".' And he went back to his personal hygiene.

From then on, he spoke to me on an irregular basis, generally when he wanted something. When I came to interview Auster, I was able to tell him that thanks to his book, Parker had now begun to talk. 'So he's able to do some of the work at last?' nodded Auster. 'That's the spirit.'

Parker was very chatty the weekend in April he turned up in Lincolnshire to find that he was no longer the only young dog on the block. My other sister, Mary, had come to stay, bringing with her a collie called Sam.

Livid with this intrusion, Parker shadowed Sam, muttering through his whiskers, his tail upright, clearly hoping to repeat his brave performance with the baby Doberman. Many times I saw him take a paw off the ground and quiver with a mixture of apprehension and excitement at the prospect of the show-down. For his part, Sam bared his teeth and sneered at Parker. Who did this pipsqueak Scottie think he was?

Thus derided, Parker took on an anxious, fatalistic look, stalking around the house like a cowardly sheriff who knows the moment of truth is coming. The crunch came on Sunday when some other family members arrived for lunch. Sam gave them a friendly sniff that Parker saw as a threat to his pack. The tail shot up, the paw quivered, and the two dogs went outside. Moments later, Parker was lying in his basket, looking shocked and Sam was limping. As it turned out, there was no damage done, but Parker was exhausted by the stress of it all and suffered a touch of the vapours. He was convinced he had won the battle and was furious when he found me throwing a ball for Sam in the garden.

'What on earth are you up to?' he squeaked. 'I've just vanquished him and now you're giving him the wrong idea.'

'I'm just playing catch,' I said. 'Isn't he good!'

'In my garden,' squeaked Parker. 'No! No! No!'

'It's not just *your* garden,' I said.

'Heh, heh,' said Sam, sneering. 'Shift it, dude. We playin' catch.'

I was surprised by Sam's American accent. He ought to have had a nice rural burr, like Phil Drabble, the late presenter of *One Man and His Dog*. But you never know what a dog's going to sound like, and he was Peter Fonda at his meanest.

Each time Sam set off after a ball, Parker chased him growling and grumbling, then trotted back proudly, fancying he had seen him off. Once, fed up with Parker's forays, the collie slunk up on him when he was having a roll on his back. Parker opened his eyes to find Sam standing over him, his yellow eyes narrow and his tongue hanging out. Parker shot off and hid behind my legs. 'Did you see that?' he said, tugging at my sock. 'The sneaky collie.'

'Heh, heh,' said Sam. 'Throw da ball.'

When Mary put her dog in the car, ready for off, I came outside to see Parker doing a Scottish victory dance round the vehicle, peeing on every tyre. 'I've got rid of him,' he said. 'Yippee!'

'You didn't do anything,' I said. 'My sister has to go, that's all.'

'More wars are won through happenstance than intention,' he said. 'The point is, I'm here and he's not. So I am the winner. Three cheers for me.'

'Heh, heh,' said Sam, leaning out the window. 'Throw da ball.'

'I don't think he cares very much,' I told Parker.

We all waved when Mary drove off. 'Wave,' I said to Parker. And on cue he lifted his right paw and jiggled it up and down. Of course – and I didn't need him to tell me this – he was only scratching himself.

For a while, Parker was king of the roost again. But his happiness was short-lived, because Lily died.

Lily was his favourite of my parents' three spaniels. She was the equivalent of eighty years old when Parker first met her, while he was barely seven in human years. From the first he adored her. She was a dizzy, affectionate, brave dog, very pretty when she was young and always fond of men. She would chase and fetch all day and when she was too arthritic to be given sticks and balls, she wandered around with a leaf or twig in her mouth, presenting it more in hope than expectation. She always had some sort of wound: a rip from barbed wire, or a blackthorn stuck in her paw, but she didn't care about pain.

Parker followed her everywhere and always made first for her when we arrived, waving his paws, ignoring her cross yelps as she protested at the attentions of her juvenile admirer.

For a long time, Lily had suffered from arthritis. Then this was complicated by a badly inflamed leg. As dogs do, she forgot about the pain when there was the prospect of a walk, but in the evening she was in agony. For a while, my parents considered having the leg amputated – some dogs get by well on three legs – but were advised that there was probably a tumour under the swelling. So, one sunny afternoon, the vet came round and Lily was carried out and put on a blanket under the trees. She was quite unafraid, went to sleep peacefully, and was buried in the shrubbery where she used to rootle.

The house became much quieter, and my parents felt her loss acutely. There were mixed reactions from the other dogs. Thomas, who was Lily's brother, a great shuffling bow-legged spaniel, talked quietly to himself. Rosie, no relation to Lily, had always been a bit jealous of her and was pleased, but also widdled all over the place. Parker went around sniffing curiously, looking for her. Reminders of Lily were everywhere. One of her habits was eating the plastic stuffing of her basket. This passed through her, and after her death, in shady places around the garden, and even on the gravel out the front, were little shreds of nylon, blowing about in the westerly wind.

12

In May, Kim discovered she was pregnant. We were both delighted but this happy occurrence posed an enormous problem. We were 6,000 miles apart and spent a fair portion of our relationship in cyber-space. But for one of us to have moved altogether to the other's world would have placed us under serious strain. Kim liked England – she was half-English – but she was used to having a substantial income from her store in LA and though things were at last going well for me in England, they were unlikely ever to go that well quickly enough. Nor could I move to America. In England, I knew who I was, even if I was only the dog-man, and I was scared at the thought of starting all over again. There was only one reason for a writer going to Los Angeles. Perhaps I was displaying a peculiarly English lack of initiative, but I knew nothing about making films and couldn't see that I'd be welcomed with open arms. We found that for all these difficulties, we really did love each other and were having a child that both of us wanted. There was no question about that.

Perhaps the double life suited us both. Perhaps we were complicated people who had come up with a complex formula for domestic contentment by avoiding it altogether. Certainly, I had become used to inhabiting with Parker a world that felt real and could be described but never threatened me with too much intimacy. I imagined it, so I controlled it. Some Hollywood people seem to go about relationships like scripts, but never know what comes after the happy marriage of the third act. There are no third acts in life, of course, there is just the living. Because we were always travelling, we were always at the first act. 'Where will you live?' asked our friends. Good question, to which I could only say that our daughter – we knew it would be a girl – would be born in Los Angeles and afterwards, we hoped that one way or another, we'd be able to make it work, to live some time here and some time there.

For the rest of the year, we shuttled to and fro. I tried to look on the eleven-hour flight to Los Angeles as being no longer than the bus-trip from London to Cornwall, and costing as much as a first-class air-fare from London to Edinburgh. It wasn't so bad, though I inevitably caught some or other bug. Not only did I miss Parker, but I was stuffed when it came to writing about him, so I tried to make the trips coincide with breaks from the column or else I wrote about the dogs of Los Angeles.

The city has two designated 'dog-parks', one of which is Runyon Canyon in the Hollywood Hills. It lies at the top of Fuller Avenue, just two blocks north of Hollywood Boulevard, in what would be the heart of town, if Los Angeles had the physiology of other towns. I went there a lot. On my first visit, I was shocked. I walked through some park gates, up a short stretch of path and found myself in a dry, scrubby mountainous landscape, populated by dogs, and decorated with signs warning me to beware of rattle snakes and mountain lions. The hike to the top of the canyon took about twenty minutes and offered wonderful views of the city's ever-receding parallel lines, best seen first thing in the morning, because by lunchtime the smog has settled over much of town. I was told that Christmas was the best time to appreciate the views, when all the cars were on holiday.

Americans love their dogs and Runyon Canyon was a very doggy place: park attendants doused the trees with odour obliterator, and there were rolls of free poo-bags (unfortunately thin and prone to split) and tin bowls of water.

Doggier still was Laurel Canyon dog-park, a fetid couple of acres of canine playground up on Mulholland Drive, the road that snakes across the top of the Hollywood Hills and one of the most romantic stretches of Los Angeles. This being LA, it is a tough kind of romance: the hills are dry and dusty, the spectacular views are spectacularly urban and the comparatively remote route connects the sites of various murders that Max had detailed to me when I'd first visited Los Angeles. Off Mulholland it was, that Roman Polanski had the house where his wife Sharon Tate was killed.

All sorts of horrors were plotted in Laurel Canyon dog-park. I overheard heists being planned and break-ins choreographed, and lengthy discussions as to whether they should shoot the husband first, or take the money *then* shoot the husband. I was at a loss as to why the place wasn't swarming with cops, until I realised that Laurel Canyon was a favourite spot for screenwriters to shoot the bull while their faithful friends barked and ran and nipped each other. Some of the packs were nominally supervised by dog-walkers whose air of beatific calm suggested that they had just enjoyed a peculiarly happy alien-abduction experience.

Laurel Canyon stank to high heaven. There were giant

pooper-scoopers available, but no amount of shovelling
could get rid of the acrid smell. Outside the park was a
sad line of Missing Dog posters fixed to the fence: all the
lost dogs seemed to be pit-bull crosses. Pit bulls, which
give the press so much lurid copy in England, are as
common in LA as happy Labs in London. I was surprised
at how even-tempered they seemed. I was grateful for
this, too, when Kim's Briard, Abelard, bit a pit bull on
the nose. I was wrestling with one of the flimsy poo-bags
and heard a squeak but imagined it was Bard that had
been bitten. The pit bull's owner laconically showed me
Bard's teeth marks on his dog's nose and advised me to
chain Bard, as 'the next time, the pit will retaliate'. The
next time! I thought it was supposed to kill, now.

I'm sure that in England the pit bulls were unlucky
with their owners. In LA, old women in sun-shades and
bifocals had them, as did executive-types and young
blondes who looked as if they'd eaten nothing but
hope for weeks. The Americans I met didn't seem
to give them studded collars or macho names, and
dogs' characters owe a good deal to their owners'
self-perception. Having a pit bull is no big deal in
Los Angeles: to be taken seriously you have to have a
pit bull *and* an M-16 rifle.

Angelenos have an ambivalent relationship with their
city, sometimes disparaging its superficiality, at other
times proud of the way the suburban crust can be
tossed aside by the underlying wilderness. Kim had
a client, a director, who lived the other side of the
Hollywood Hills. He was a pet-lover, and had two cats
which came and went as they pleased. He talked a lot
on the phone about his cats. One day Kim went over
to discuss business with him. When she arrived, he took
her immediately out into the garden and showed her a

piece of stomach lining and two little collars with bells – all the coyotes had left of his pets.

I went over to LA to see Kim in the spring, in the summer and again in the autumn. Each time, Parker went to stay in Lincolnshire, and I would telephone frequently and receive reports on his well-being, how many rabbits he had caught, whether he had been involved in any trouble. Sometimes I tried to speak to him on the telephone, but the sound of my disembodied voice would set him scurrying around looking for me. This was a pity, when I wanted to tell him snippets of news I knew he'd enjoy, for example that I'd just heard that Brock had been arrested by the police for going into the Round Pond in Kensington Gardens.

I once saw an advertisement in Los Angeles for a psychic who claimed to give over-the-phone readings on your pet, but I couldn't quite sum up the nerve to indulge. No doubt she would have told me what I already knew: that Parker was well, puzzled by my absence but had matched up the pains and gains and found Lincolnshire life was to his liking. Still, London was best for sniffs, and he was always pleased to hit the streets again and square up to his old enemies.

There was no doubt that Parker had grown up, had become a more sophisticated personality, his puppy charm overlaid by accumulated knowledge, desires, preferences, and intentions. Perhaps it's a reflection on my human nature that I credited him with adult sophistication when I realised that he could lie. Some people think that dogs don't lie: to say the thing that is not is a human characteristic. But I'd come to see that nature is full of natural liars, of insects that pretend to be twigs, of fish that pretend to be stones, and predators that pretend to be friendly.

When it came to scrapping I was alert to Parker's intentions through watching his tail and his front right paw, that trembled and hovered off the ground in the moments preceding an assault; at these tell-tale signs I would drag him away. Cottoning on to this he began to tell lies with his tail, playing wag-wag until I let him get within range.

I think he got the idea from Scottie the Scottie, who was a terrible liar.

We first came across Scottie down by Notting Hill Gate Tube. His owner was lurking outside a florist's, the thumb of his right hand swathed in a large white bandage. At his feet lay a chunky little Scottie with a grey muzzle and a grave demeanour. 'He's called Scottie,' said the owner, 'and he just bit me.'

I wasn't at all keen that Parker should go near Scottie but the other dog assumed such a benign expression, and wagged in such an engaging, friendly way, that I relented and let Parker an inch closer. Most dogs, in my experience, have a quick sniff before they go on the offensive, but Scottie was working to a premeditated plan of attack, for he promptly dropped all pretence at friendliness, and flung himself at Parker with a blood-curdling scream, kilt over his head. Parker retaliated and very quickly a crowd gathered, taking bets on the likely winner.

Because of his temperamental deficiency, Scottie wasn't allowed off the leash and had therefore worked out a way to reel the suckers to him for a spot of the biffing he so enjoyed. It was an old trick of Scottie's and generally very successful, for he tried it again on Parker, some months later, when he sighted him on Ladbroke Road. Again he wagged and lay down, looking as if butter wouldn't melt in his mouth. This time Parker was prepared.

There were nicer Scotties around, but precious few: there was Mrs Scottie, who lived near the park, but she was old and blind. Then there were Olive and Nellie, the two little Scottie Girls, who Parker met one happy day near the Round Pond. They had it all – looks, youth, personality. He wanted to ask them back for a biscuit, but they were being chaperoned and left when their owner went back to work. Sadly, he never saw them again.

After Lily's death, I thought I ought to make a serious attempt to find Parker a girlfriend closer to him in age than the old spaniel had been, and from his own breed. I finally fixed him a date with a Scottie called Skye Pilot, who lived on an idyllic riverbank in Hampshire. Two years older than him, she was a fine specimen: obstinate, talkative and a great sniffer with a bottle-brush tail and a shaggy coat. At a distance she looked the spitting image of Parker, though her nose was shorter and she was on the tubby side. 'Hormones,' muttered Penny, her owner. 'She was on the pill last season.'

This was Skye's first time too, and the occasion was marred by inexperience and reluctance. Parker seemed as though he might work it out given half a chance, but Skye was having none of it and bit him: wisps of fur floated across the kitchen floor.

'Perhaps she won't do it if you're watching?' I suggested to Penny. We went off to the pub, leaving them alone. When we returned, their attitude did not suggest any progress: Skye was in her basket, bottom to the wall, and Parker was lying at her feet, gooey eyed. We took them for a walk and they did seem to be getting on better, so I agreed to leave him there for the night.

I knew nothing about dog-breeding, so it came as no surprise when a friend of Penny's told her that we'd got it all wrong in presenting Parker as a gentleman caller. The bitch should go to the dog. It was decided that when Penny returned Parker to me, she would also leave Skye.

'They slept on separate sofas,' Penny told me when she appeared the next morning, 'but Parker seems to be getting the idea. He tried to roger my arm.'

Parker was pleased with the new bodily motion he had discovered and showed me straight away. Skye remained unimpressed and the day passed painfully.

Back in West London, Parker talked to Skye, he waved at her, he got out his tuggy-toy and shook it fiercely to show her what a brave boy he was. He let her drink first, gave up the sofa to her and when we went for walks, he showed her his favourite sniffs and protected her against strangers.

Skye trotted on regardless. She was more than able to look after herself. When we met a nasty pinscher from round the corner that had often plagued Parker, her eyes lit up with fury. She looked as if she could have eaten the other dog. As it happened, food was her main interest. She ate everything she was offered and licked out Parker's bowl three times, though it was spotlessly clean.

Eventually, Parker's frustration boiled over. He grabbed a cushion in a passionate embrace, indulged in brief onanistic frenzy and slumped down in depressed gloom. What was it Shakespeare wrote? '*The expense of spirit in a waste of shame . . .*'

When Penny and her daughter collected Skye, Parker wanted to show them both what he had learned. But the true object of his affection, who didn't want his puppies foisted on her, trotted off into the night.

After the door closed, Parker ran around looking for

Skye, sniffing frantically and whimpering. Then he went and sat by the door and howled: he'd never howled before. The sound was long and sad: '*arooo-ow-ow-ow-ooooh.*'

For twenty-four hours he languished. Eventually, her scent faded and his spirits returned. It was not all bad news: he had discovered that the strange bodily sensation that gave so much pleasure could occur even when Skye was not there. Life was never quite the same again.

Perhaps it was all the coming and going, but whenever I returned to West London I was acutely aware of the way in which the area was changing fast. After the film *Notting Hill* came out, the pace of change seemed to double – at least, this was what everyone said. Certainly, it brought an influx of tourists looking for the bookshop where Hugh Grant met Julia Roberts. That was as much as I knew about the film, as I never saw it. I knew that *he* lived in Notting Hill, and *she* lived in Beverly Hills, and from my own experience I could tell that this was only intermittently a comedy.

Parker noticed the changes too. Several of his favourite old sniffs came under threat as smelly old corners were covered with scaffolding, and we were both very disappointed when the Peppermill Supermarket on the Portobello closed its shutters for the last time. The Peppermill was a complete antidote to the encroaching delicatessen way of life. Its long, grimly lit and spartan interior held perhaps a hundred different branded goods, all arranged under fluorescent stars that read: *Rice, Biscuit, Jam* and *Dog.* I rarely found anything for myself in there, but it was handy for dog-food and they had mixer in manageable boxes, an item that sometimes seemed so rare that Lucy and I swapped notes on where we'd seen it.

One day, the shutters never went up on the Peppermill. It was sold, so the rumour went, to be part of another fashionable eatery-type development, incorporating the old Electric Cinema that stood next door, its swagged and bowed Deco façade encrusted with old posters and graffiti.

One reason I liked the Peppermill was that I could chain Parker outside it. The owners didn't have any particular liking for dogs, but you could loop a chain round the supports for their steel shutter, while *Buy Best* across the road had no external fixtures at all, and rarely got my custom. These are the kind of things that really shape consumer patterns: convenience, not advertising or good value. The availability of a dog-park facility determined Parker's diet. He sampled dozens of different brands of canned food and mixer, some of which he has enjoyed more than others. Wholegrain mixer had to be his least favourite, while anything with tripe in it scored highly. Nothing has ever been more delicious than the 'dried meat' I used to buy from the farm suppliers in Wales. I dread to think what it contained; it looked like the scrapings from a prehistoric grave. It also had unfortunate side effects, and was not for use in enclosed spaces.

For a while I had a handy device called a 'Lim Pet' that a reader sent me. It was a sucker-type thing you could slap on walls outside shops and chain your dog to. Inevitably I left it stuck somewhere in West London.

Change also extended into Kensington Gardens, where some paths were closed and grassed over while throughout the summer work proceeded on what seemed to be the development of a dual carriageway around the Round

Pond. When it finally opened it catered for a new class of dog-joggers and pram-joggers. Life had been tough enough for a dog, what with the roller-bladers and skate-boarders and mountain-bikers. Later, the children's playground closed for redevelopment into a themed amusement area. It was very American, but then the area was full of Americans, while Los Angeles was full of Brits. A population exchange was taking place, and more than that. The Americans we met in London were always wonderfully well-mannered, while the Brits in Los Angeles seemed to have embraced some of the worst vulgarity of the place.

The Americans loved Scotties and we once met three couples in the space of an hour who had or used to have Scottie dogs and they too said, 'You don't see many of them nowadays.' And, 'We always had one when we were kids.' Kate, a fellow Scottie-owner, alerted me to the existence of American Scottie websites, where I learned a crucial word of Scottie vocabulary, the 'Arooo!' After I became aware of this noise, I heard Parker make it many times, accompanied by a long dog-stretch.

At times it seemed the unreality one sensed about Notting Hill was becoming the reality: the actors were now the people and the public had become visitors to the set. The area was fluid and slippery and I lost my bearings as landmarks disappeared. In any case, I was so off in my own world half the time I was the last person to know about the latest place to go, and rarely able to find it anyway. Walking Parker around for much of the day, I ought to have been familiar with the local geography. In practice, though I carried a book of routes in my head, these had few street-names attached, because I was never really going anywhere, just following the dog, who moved in his own abstract world. All the same, I was too proud to admit I didn't know my way around.

One day we were walking up some street, possibly Colville Terrace, when a swish black car pulled up, the rear window went down and a woman in a scarf and dark glasses – perhaps it was Julia Roberts *incognito* – asked me if I could 'tell her driver the way to Powis Square'.

'Go left on Ledbury Road,' I said, 'then second left up some other street, then right . . .'

'No, no,' hissed Parker. 'I wish you'd stop doing this.'

'Quiet,' I said. 'Not in public.'

He scratched behind his ear. 'All right,' he said, 'don't listen. But you're forever misdirecting people. Just admit you don't know.'

This was a painful truth. Acting with the best intentions, I must nonetheless have misdirected several hundred tourists.

The woman was looking on, surprised. 'Is anything the matter?' she asked. 'You're talking to the pavement.'

'It's quite all right,' I said. 'Just go left, third left, then abandon the car and walk.'

They set off into the wilderness. Parker yawned and sniffed at the base of a tree. 'My goodness,' he said, 'approximately two hours and twenty-three minutes ago, a Cairn terrier with some Jack Russell in it came along here. Owner probably thinks it's pedigree. If you'd only ask me. It's easy to find Powis Square, or Three Trees as we call it. You go up Monster McTavish Avenue, along The Street of Great Stinks, cross the road at Furry Gutter, and bingo, you're there.'

We had our own city. Like many things in my life, it was part real, part in my head.

*   *   *

We didn't stay in West London all the time when I was back from America. I tried to make sure that we had some sort of adventure, so Parker would remember that he always had a good time with me. When Kim came over in May, we went to Scotland, where he was greeted with his own basket at the Ballathie House Hotel in Perthshire, was stung by a bee and had a terrifying encounter with a stray lamb out on the seashore by Oban. We rented a cottage there, and Parker lay on the doorstep, growling at the Western Isles, that looked by a trick of perspective as if they were vast shaggy cattle creeping up on us.

Later in the summer, I took Parker back to Allihies in Ireland, where we had stayed in a tent a year before. Just one human year, but seven years of his little life. His childhood memories seemed intact for he hopped from the car and straightaway made for the spot where we pitched our tent the previous August. Scuffing up a fountain of grass, he gave me a great stinky lick and scuttled off along the beach, hooting his arrival to the gulls and the waves.

We didn't camp this time. I rented a caravan from Anthony O'Sullivan the postman from the farm across the road, so I had a table to work on and Parker had a doorstep to guard.

It was quiet at first, nothing but wind and rain and sea and a hot sun coming and going in between. On Friday night, peace was shattered when the hob-goblins arrived from Cork. There was a multitude of these carrot-topped creatures and shortly after arriving their parents abandoned them and went off to the pubs in Allihies. The goblins got up to much cheerful wickedness, banging on doors and running away, and the next morning, Mr P's steel bowl was missing. Tracking down the goblins to a small tent I asked for my dog-bowl back.

'It wasn't us, mister,' said a small goblin.

'We don't know anything about it,' said the chief goblin, silencing his junior with a stern look.

'Oh well,' I said, 'if you do ever find out where it is, I'd be pleased to have it back. And you won't bang on my door at midnight again, will you?'

'No, mister,' said the junior goblin.

'We can't say,' said the chief triumphantly, 'because it wasn't us that did it this time, was it?'

'If you do find the bowl,' I said, 'I'll give you two pounds.'

This offer provoked a great deal of urgent conference. Later that afternoon, Parker's growl heralded the arrival on my doorstep of the chief goblin.

'We found this,' he said, 'in the hedge.'

It was a bowl like Parker's, but it was older and rusty, as if it had been used as a drip-tray. My suspicions were aroused, but the goblin was insistent he had not filched the bowl and I didn't have the heart to deny him his reward, which he spent on a mass of sticky sweets. I had a feeling this was not the last of the bowl business.

There were plenty of other dogs for Parker to play with: small dogs from the village who attached themselves to day-trippers, sheepdogs who came down to swim, their hair matted and streaked from the salt and sun. There was a dog with three legs that saw off Parker, and a collie that ran up and down in the surf all day, yapping at bubbles.

Parker even went in the water. There were two Labrador bitches wading in the bay, and he was so determined to get a sniff that he looked plaintively at me, gave a sad squeak to say, 'So long if it all goes wrong,' and hopped in.

Walking along the cliffs in the evening, I heard wild, sad barking and thought I could make out the shape of a large black dog, running up the coast. Sometimes it stood on the little quay, next it would appear on rocks that jutted out into the sea. Parker gave a warning growl and the dog suddenly came out of the dark fields in front of us, flowing over the tumble-down drystone walls. It gave us a wide berth and Parker gave chase, but it went places he would not follow, on to razor-back promontories and narrow sheep-tracks.

It was all a touch spooky and I was on the verge of chalking this up as a second canine spectre, when I saw the dog stuffed into the front window of Anthony O'Sullivan's house. Not only was he a postman but he also had lobster pots out in the bay. The dog mystery was solved when I saw the hound follow him down to the quay, where it stayed while he chugged off across the grey water. The dog watched him dwindle into the distance, then set off up the coast, keeping level with the boat. It never left its vigil, nor stopped barking encouragement until it saw the boat carrying its master come chugging back again.

At nights, Parker became reluctant to go far into the fields along the coast. He's never refused a walk, so I wondered if there was after all some sort of supernatural atmosphere pervading the surrounding ancient ruins. Walking there in the day, I realised that it was nothing of the sort. The fields were covered with whinbushes – tiny gorse plants – that Parker couldn't see at night. He wasn't afraid of a ghost, merely of pricking his little paddy-paws.

The goblins stayed for a few days but troubled us no

further. One day, Parker and I went off on an excursion and returned to find the goblin families had vanished, and so had Mr P's water bowl. Its contents had been apologetically transferred to an old pan I had left out to dry. In the evening, Parker lingered, sniffing by an adjacent, shuttered caravan. Through the attached awning, I thought I could glimpse a steel bowl under the edge of the caravan, with a hose running down into it. It was, as I had thought, a drip tray.

No doubt the chief goblin had told his parents that the bowl had been loaned to me. I doubt he mentioned the two pounds. I thought he was a little goblin genius.

Even in London, summer wasn't so bad. The undergrowth on Hampstead Heath ran wild, and the waist-high grass, cow parsley and briars created hundreds of secret areas and new paths. Though I must have walked every inch of the Heath, it suddenly seemed entirely new and strange and vast. For Parker, it was a dog paradise of countryside with metropolitan sniffs. The sun brought out the crazies in Kensington Gardens: a pair of Wiccan tree-worshippers, and a sweet Japanese girl who, lacking a dog to walk, carried around a photo-album of the dog she had in Japan, showing the pictures to other dog-owners, and an old woman with mad black eyes who wore a red dressing gown and had a rheumatic mutt called Betty, who she was forever trying to pimp to passing dogs.

'Oh, a Scottie!' she shrieked in delight, when she saw Parker. 'Oh, Betty loves the Scotties 'cos they always try and ride her. Have a good sniff! Betty loves that.' Cackling wildly, she waxed on about all the other lovely things Parker was welcome to do to Betty if he had a moment.

Parker seemed put off by this graphic enthusiasm, for he took to hiding from Betty and her mad mistress.

For a while he had a fascination for the entrance to the Russian Consulate on the Bayswater Road, as if this shadowy stretch of pavement, overhung by horse chest-nuts and edged by tall shabby iron gates, was inscribed with strange Cyrillic scents. He also liked the other former Communist stronghold of the Czech visa section, a little bit up the road. I felt a bit self-conscious lingering outside these places, while Parker rifled through his dead-letter boxes. Perhaps, somewhere in Moscow there was on file a fuzzy photograph of Parker with a question mark beside it. I knew for a fact that there was one secret dossier on him. The dog-groomers I now used kept notes on their customers, and on one visit I happened by chance to see a profile of a dog, lying on the counter. *Very growly*, I read. I asked what they'd written down for Parker, but the staff were embarrassed and made various excuses. He didn't like that groomers at all, and I imagine that at the very least the secret Parker files read *quite growly*.

The year passed quickly. Soon, people were returning from their summer holidays, brown and full of stories and good intentions. I rarely seemed to see half my old friends, even the ones who lived just up the road. Notting Hill is like that. People have their little rounds and habits and you can live a few hundred yards from someone and lose touch with them. I knew Belle had fallen in love with a fashionable pastry-cook and all but wasted away, sitting in his café consuming nothing but cappuccino. Max was devoting a year to charity work and was flying off to distant African destinations, where there were no hotels at all to look at. Adèle, who had been almost theologically opposed to wedlock, got engaged, to her surprise. I found her sitting in a pub in a state of shock after a visit to Peter Jones to do the gift list. 'I was sober when I agreed,' she said. She told me she was going to run away just before the ceremony, to live in a village in Cornwall called Prozac. I almost believed her.

Soon there were autumn storms and the first skeletons of dead leaves appeared, pressed into the pavements. I caught the usual flu and lay in bed, drifting in and out of consciousness, listening to the news that two Japanese girls had been found dead in Hyde Park. They were holding hands under a tree when it was struck by a fork of lightning. The poor girls lay undiscovered in the wet grass all night, while thousands swept along the road only yards away. Perhaps they were found by someone walking a dog. It is one of the fears of dog-walkers that they will stumble across tragedy, because of that dour, familiar line from the news: 'The body was discovered by a man walking his dog . . .'

Often I woke up, shocked to think that I was about to become a father. Though I fancied I was alert to the practical side of pregnancy and what fatherhood would entail, I found that I could not understand what was happening biologically. I discovered that at some level, I had always thought that my genes were reluctant to further themselves, then it had always struck me as an act of incredible confidence to put a child into the world, and I doubted my own confidence. If you believed, as I did, that the only true stories were really those of unravelling and disintegration, then how did the progress of a child fit into this pessimistic view? At the bottom of it all was fear that whatever good happened to me, it would sooner or later be taken away.

However, it was going to happen, whether I believed it or not. Kim said our baby was due towards the end of January, and I booked a flight out to Los Angeles for the middle of December.

Before I left, I took Parker off for one last weekend in Herefordshire, near where we had once lived. This time, I told him, as we drove down, I would be away for a long time. He looked at me, puzzled but anxious at the tone of my voice, and wagged his tail.

The trip was for myself as much as him, for walking is frowned upon in Los Angeles and I was determined to pack in a few miles. I found a pub at Goodrich that accepted dogs and booked in for a couple of nights. Goodrich is a village on the Wye, best known for its castle, which was taken by the Parliamentary forces under Colonel John Birch in 1646. The story goes that Birch's niece was in the castle with her beloved, the royalist Charles Clifford. The couple tried to escape, but drowned in the river, and when the wind blows you can still hear them shrieking.

The winds blew and the ghosts shrieked as we walked first up Coppet Hill in Herefordshire then crossed to Wales to stagger up the Skirrid. We did about ten miles in all, in sun, rain and snow, but Parker was good for another ten. He rolled in the frosty meadows by the Wye and at the top of the Skirrid, where the wind knocked me to and fro, he rolled again and kicked his legs in pleasure. The Borders are a strange compelling area, alive with the shifting moods in the weather, the sudden changes in countryside, language and culture, the jagged debris of civil wars and the quiet green valleys. From the top of the Skirrid, late in the afternoon, I saw sun on the fields of Herefordshire to the east while from the west, dark clouds marched towards us from the Black Mountains. One moment we stood at the centre of a brilliant sunset, the next we were shrouded by a hailstorm.

After the days walking I found a pub that didn't mind having Mr P propping up the bottom of the bar, and fell into conversation with a weekending Londoner, who was amused to find the dog that wrote for the *Daily Telegraph.* I told him it was no novelty. I remembered from the days when I occasionally edited the Letters page of the *Telegraph,* that it was the considered opinion of some readers that the paper had for years been written by dogs.

This cheerful man told me he was a marketing executive. He wasn't a dog-owner himself, and was curious about why people had them. 'What is a dog?' he asked me. 'Why do people want dogs?'

I ran through the usual reasons. Dogs were furry companions that gave unqualified affection; they could also be large defence mechanisms. They were loyal and loving. They took the place of grown-up children or taught small children about positive relationships.

He shook his head. 'When I think of Dog, I see something else. You see, my father always used to say that he was "going to see a man about a dog" when what he really meant was that he was going off to the pub. So when I try to picture Dog, I see a pint of bitter. When I think of my father I see a pint of bitter, too.'

I agreed that dogs were essential to the domestic set-up, providing people with a secret life outside the home.

'Yes, that's what I think a dog's for,' agreed my new friend. 'It's an excuse. An endearing excuse. The excuse your loved one will accept. There's no point in me having a dog, because I'm not married and don't have to excuse myself to anybody.'

I asked him if he'd ever get a dog. 'Oh yes,' he said. 'When I've got kids, I'm going to have an Australian cattle-dog, which will require tons of exercise. And I'm going to call it Alibi.'

Parker yawned and stretched. It had been a long day and he wanted his dinner. Someone had dropped fag-ash on him, and he had grey hair.

'What does Parker do for you?' the man asked suddenly. 'You don't need to escape from anyone, do you?'

No, I didn't have to try and escape from someone who was 6,000 miles away. 'Only myself,' I replied, 'and he's good for that. But when you ask what is he for? I'd say, like many of the best things, he's practically useless but emotionally essential.'

A third man came over and slapped the cheerful executive on the back. 'Hello, Joe,' he said. 'Look, that dog, would you believe it, writes a column for the *Telegraph*! Speaks too! Ho ho ho!'

Parker's real job, of course, was to make people laugh.

Later on, I snaffled my steak upstairs for Parker. Our room was a twin suite and he had a bed all to himself. He was a happy Scottie, and happier still when I took him to Lincolnshire a few days later.

I had to leave at five in the morning to catch my flight and stole out through the kitchen where Parker was asleep on his favourite chair, surrounded by his dog friends. He looked up at me, yawned, and thumped his tail. 'I'll be back in the New Year,' I said to him, but he was already asleep.

A few hours later, I was asleep too, somewhere above Greenland.

'The festive season' in Los Angeles was a bewildering mixture of the trivial and the apocalyptic: vast plastic Santas marched across the roofs of the shopping malls, while religious fanatics took out a full-page advert in the *LA Times*, saying the end of the world was nigh, because for two thousand years we had been going to church on Sunday when God had meant it to be Thursday. Despite our other wickedness God had us on a legal technicality. There was something very American about that. They rarely get the gangsters for murder, but tax evasion.

I heard that Parker was happy in Lincolnshire, where everything was the colour of wet burned straw and the only sound was the rusty cough of roosting pheasants. 'Oh, he's fine,' said my mother. 'Doesn't miss you one little bit.' All very reassuring.

Kim and I waited for the birth of our daughter. It wasn't too bad a wait. We had a nice LA Christmas: a lunch-party at which various thin people ate in public, a nine-foot tree, Bing Crosby, movies, movies, and more movies. For New Year's Eve, we drove to a party at Malibu. Danny our host was a genius-composer-sicko. On a previous visit, I was introduced to his cat Frisky, and lovingly stroked the curled-up tabby before I realised it was stuffed.

Danny had a large collection of skulls and dried heads. His Christmas tree was decorated with cheesy devils and plastic surfers. He had a dog, too, an affectionate Australian shepherd called Gus. Like many Californians,

Gus had a weight problem. In an attempt to ensure he exercised, he was sent every week to sheepherding classes. He was an excellent pupil and had a certificate in sheepherding.

Danny adored Gus and intended that he should never be parted from him. He showed me a cutting advertising a company called Friends Forever in Minnesota, that will freeze-dry pets. A client who had his poodle Sweetie Pie frozen, was quoted as saying, 'They told me she would look like she's just lying there sleeping, and she does.' Again, how reassuring.

Over the holiday, Los Angeles fell silent, its population of cars tucked up in driveways and garages, dreaming of their next valet-cleaning. Bicycling to the office I rented I heard birdsong and smelled clean air. The sun shone gently, for once without a lens of poisonous fumes. Walking Kim's dogs up Runyon Canyon I could, as promised, see the drama of the city's setting, from the mountains to the blue of the Pacific.

Los Angeles could be a fine place to live, if only the humans could overthrow the cars by which they are enslaved.

We knew that our daughter would be along around the end of January, but there was every chance she'd pop by sooner if the fancy took her, so each pang Kim felt had my heart thumping, wondering if the bags were packed and if I could remember the way to the Cedars-Sinai Hospital. When the tension drove me stir-crazy, I went up the coast to Big Sur to go walking among the Redwoods and look for grey whales swimming down the coast to their breeding grounds off Mexico. Kim couldn't travel, and of course I didn't have Mr P, so it was lonely. After two days, I came out in spots and felt it imperative that I return home. There were still three weeks to the birth, but I drove the 300 miles back that night. Twenty-four hours later, Kim woke up, said she felt crampy, and then the pains began, every ten minutes.

Her intention had been to try a Californian technique called 'hypno-birthing', putting herself into a trance and, as her tapes suggested, 'letting her beautiful baby open her cervix like a flower'. She managed for several hours until the pain required anaesthetic, and here came the problem: she believed she was allergic to what was on offer for the epidural. They suggested that they tried some scratch tests, and she agreed, though a reaction would have closed her throat.

It all became a bit tense. They decided to administer the epidural, and were putting in tubes and things and there seemed to be too many people in the small room, so I went for a walk.

I was afraid. How I wished I had my dog, with his silly wagging tail and stinky whiskers. The fear nagged me. I'd never really believed that I would be a father. I just wasn't cut out for it. I was dreaming all this.

I'm not making this up. There, on the plaza of the hospital, was a Scottie. It was tied to a post waiting for its owner. It pricked up its ears at me, sniffed about, and gave me an 'Arooooo'. I laughed and stayed with the dog for a few minutes. I thought of Parker and all the silly, funny times I'd had with him, and how above all he accepted what life offered and was never despondent for long. I felt a whole lot better. It was all going to be fine. Of course it would be fine. This was real life and nothing could stop it happening.

Nine hours later, at 2.24 a.m., little Georgina dropped into the world. I had an extraordinary moment, when the faces of every relation I'd known passed in front of me, as her waxy face took its first breath and she screamed for life. Then she was suddenly no one else but my daughter, an irrefutable fact in my life, someone who was part of me, for whom I would never have to imagine a voice. A daughter: a family. And the family dog.

I was grown up. I was no longer just Parker's 'dad'.

I just hoped she wouldn't pull his whiskers.

SOME WEEKS LATER

After collecting more air-miles in her first three months than I did in my first thirty years, my daughter Georgie arrived in England with Kim on a wet day in March. Her first encounter with Parker was in Lincolnshire, where he had been billeted with my parents' spaniels while I went to pick up the new arrivals. The meeting was a confusing affair. As usual, Parker jumped up to greet me and was surprised to discover a small, fair-haired creature in my arms.

'You've brought a Norfolk terrier home,' he said. 'You've got a puppy. Cooee!'

'She's not a Norfolk terrier,' I said. 'She's a baby.'

'Oh no,' he said. 'That's not a baby. You can't have a baby. That's a Norfolk terrier. I know one of those when I see one. It's short, fair-haired, with a big rear end. That is definitely a Norfolk terrier.'

I put the Norfolk terrier down and he came over to have a good sniff. The puppy beamed at her new surroundings, rolled her big blue eyes at Parker, gave a gaseous yawn and passed out. Parker wagged his tail and wiggled his ears, but there was no response. He hopped up and confided in me.

'It's not quite what I had in mind,' he said. 'She's a bit disappointing. Perhaps she'll cheer up later. Where did you get her? Do they really come from Norfolk? Has she had her tail docked?'

The pale, supine figure suddenly opened her mouth, shot her arms in the air and let out a terrible cry of hunger. Not just Parker, but all the dogs and cats fled and huddled in baskets and under chairs. They watched in horror as the humans flew around to tend to the small creature. A baby had arrived.

Parker was going through a minor crisis in any case. Hanging out with my parents' spaniels he'd picked up some filthy spaniel ways. Apart from a childhood interest in the contents of the cat-litter box, he's never been a great scrounger of rubbish, but during this stay in Lincolnshire he had been seen chewing on pieces of old rabbit in the adjacent fields and had become first in the begging queue whenever there was the prospect of kitchen scraps. Sadly, he was even spotted hanging around the cat-litter tray, with a hangdog expression, like a former soak hesitating at the entrance to a pub. He needed some terrier company, hence his hopes for Georgie.

His attitude to the Norfolk terrier was confused, just as his first response to Kim had been confused. He would run upstairs to find mother and baby, give them big kisses and curl up at their feet, but when I appeared, he put his ears back and retreated. I know pets will be jealous when children first come along. Perhaps he was troubled by the thought he might be seen as disloyal to me if he was loyal to them, or worried that he might be edging in on my pack, or that he was being edged out – or perhaps he wanted *me* to feel a little guilty. Everything is fine with Parker so long as he has his walks, and his old blanket, but I'd forgotten the blanket and for a few days the biological imperatives of parenthood meant that I just couldn't find time for long walks. The weather was dreadful too, and perhaps he blamed it all on the new arrival.

One morning my daughter's pram was in the kitchen when I went downstairs to make tea. It was a big pram, of American manufacture, a Chevrolet among prams, and Georgie enjoyed being bounced in it very much; however, she was upstairs snoozing with her mother, so it was a shock when I saw a pair of huge liquid eyes staring out from the warm dark depths of the pram's blue fleece lining.

'Parker,' I said. 'Is that you?'

The shadows moved and slowly formed a recognisable shape: a pair of tall ears, a long hooter and some tusky whiskers, rather like the wolf under Granny's bonnet in *Little Red Riding Hood.* It was Parker all right, though how he had got in there I don't know. It was a three-foot vertical jump. It showed the pram must be stable, I noted in my sleep-fuddled, child-obsessed mind. Parker yawned, stretched and regarded me complacently. There was only one baby in my life, he seemed to be saying, and always would be; the other was definitely a Norfolk terrier.

CHANGE WHERE YOUR MONEY LIVES,
CHANGE HOW YOUR FINANCIAL WORLD GROWS

MONEY
MOVES

TARA NOLAN

Money Moves: Change Where Your Money Lives,
Change How Your Financial World Grows
By Tara Nolan

© 2022 DARC Press, Inc.

DARC Press
P.O. Box 591
Peyton, Colorado 80831
www.nolanfinancialpartners.com

ISBN (paperback): 978-0-9845414-0-9
ISBN (ebook): 979-8-9855805-0-1
Library of Congress Control Number: 2022901387

Disclaimer: The information contained in this book is for informational purposes
only and not intended to take the place of in-person professional guidance. It is
intended to provide the connective tissue or framework—through stories—to
think about what financial success feels like for you and give you good questions to
ask when cocreating a plan with a professional for abundance in your life. It should
not be considered legal or financial advice. You should consult with an attorney
or tax professional to determine what may be best for your individual needs.

Our books may be purchased in bulk for educational or business use.
Please contact your local bookseller or DARC Press at 1 (719) 210-
4242, or by email at wealth@nolanfinancialpartners.com.

Edited by AJ Harper and Zoë Bird
Proofread by Linda Morris
Typeset by Choi Messer
Cover design by Choi Messer

Printed in the United States of America
10 9 8 7 6 5 4 3 2 1